Andrew Merson

GCSE OCR Gateway
Biology
Higher Revision Guide

This book is for anyone doing **GCSE OCR Gateway Biology** at higher level.

GCSE Science is all about **understanding how science works**.
And not only that — understanding it well enough to be able to **question**
what you hear on TV and read in the papers.

But you can't do that without a fair chunk of **background knowledge**. Hmm, tricky.

Happily this CGP book includes all the **science facts** you need to learn,
and shows you how they work in the **real world**. And in true CGP style,
we've explained it all as **clearly and concisely** as possible.

It's also got some daft bits in to try and make the whole
experience at least vaguely entertaining for you.

<u>What CGP is all about</u>

Our sole aim here at CGP is to produce the highest
quality books — carefully written, immaculately presented
and dangerously close to being funny.

Then we work our socks off to get them out to you — at the cheapest possible prices.

Contents

MODULE B4 — IT'S A GREEN WORLD

MODULE B5 — THE LIVING BODY

MODULE B6 — BEYOND THE MICROSCOPE

EXAM SKILLS

Published by Coordination Group Publications Ltd.

Editors:
Ellen Bowness, Gemma Hallam, Sharon Keeley, Andy Park, Kate Redmond,
Katherine Reed, Alan Rix, Ami Snelling, Claire Thompson, Julie Wakeling.

Contributors:
Gloria Barnett, Sandy Gardner, Julian Hardwick, Derek Harvey, Richard Parsons,
Stephen Phillips, Claire Reed, Adrian Schmit, Claire Stebbing.

ISBN: 978 1 84146 670 5

With thanks to Vanessa Aris and Glenn Rogers for the proofreading.
With thanks to Laura Phillips for the copyright research.
With thanks to Tom D. Thacher, M.D., for permission to reproduce the photograph on page 4.

Groovy website: www.cgpbooks.co.uk

Printed by Elanders Hindson Ltd, Newcastle upon Tyne.
Jolly bits of clipart from CorelDRAW®

Fitness and Blood Pressure

If you've ever wondered what the docs on Casualty are on about when they say in excited voices that someone's blood pressure is "92 over 60" or something... well, you're about to find out.

Being Fit is Not the Same as Being Healthy

1) Make sure you know the difference between being fit and being healthy...

> **HEALTHY** means being free of any infections or diseases, whereas being **FIT** is a measure of how well you can perform physical tasks.

2) Fitness is not a precise term and it can be measured in different ways.

3) Fitness profiles measure strength, speed and flexibility, together with stamina.

Stamina is how long you can keep going.

4) Stamina is a good indication of cardiovascular efficiency (the ability of the heart to supply the muscles with oxygen). It can be tested by measuring oxygen uptake during exercise, and blood pressure.

Blood is Pumped Around Your Body Under Pressure

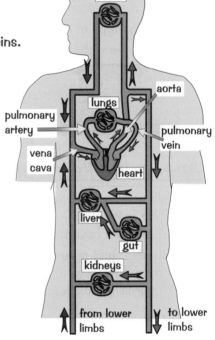

1) The blood is pumped around the body by the contractions of the heart. These contractions increase the pressure of the blood.

2) The blood leaves the heart and flows through arteries. These split into thousands of tiny capillaries, which take blood to every cell in the body. The blood then flows back to the heart through veins. The pressure gets lower as the blood flows through the system.

3) The blood pressure is at its highest when the heart contracts — this is the systolic pressure. When the heart relaxes, the pressure is at its lowest — this is the diastolic pressure.

4) Blood pressure is measured in mm of mercury (mmHg).

5) In a healthy person it shouldn't be higher than about 135 (systolic pressure) over about 85 (diastolic pressure).

6) As people get older, their blood pressure tends to get higher. Other factors that contribute to high blood pressure are:

- a diet with too much salt in it
- being overweight
- drinking too much alcohol
- being under lots of stress for a long time
- not doing enough exercise

High or Low Blood Pressure Can Cause Health Problems

1) If the pressure of the blood is too high it can cause blood vessels to burst, and this can lead to strokes, brain damage and kidney damage.

2) High blood pressure can be corrected by lifestyle changes — consuming less salt and alcohol, doing more exercise and losing weight, etc. In extreme cases, drugs are used to help correct the problem.

3) Low blood pressure is much less common than high blood pressure, but it can also cause problems. It causes poor circulation and tissues don't get all the food and oxygen they need. If your brain doesn't get enough food and oxygen you'll get dizzy and end up fainting.

Don't let Exam stress send your blood pressure through the roof...

The factors mentioned above only increase the likelihood of someone developing high blood pressure. None of them will definitely give them high blood pressure. So someone who pours salt on every meal and never exercises might have perfectly healthy blood pressure. But... they'd be less likely to suffer problems if they had a healthier diet and took more exercise. It all comes down to probabilities.

Respiration

You need <u>energy</u> to keep your body going. Energy comes from <u>food</u>, and it's <u>released</u> by <u>respiration</u>.

Respiration *is NOT "Breathing In and Out"*

1) Respiration is <u>NOT</u> breathing in and breathing out, as you might think.

2) <u>Respiration</u> actually goes on in <u>every cell</u> in your body.

3) It's the process of <u>releasing energy</u> from <u>glucose</u>.

4) There are <u>two types</u> of respiration, <u>aerobic</u> and <u>anaerobic</u>.

This energy is used to do things like:
- build up <u>larger molecules</u> (like proteins)
- contract <u>muscles</u>
- maintain a steady <u>body temperature</u>

> **RESPIRATION is the process of RELEASING ENERGY from GLUCOSE, which happens constantly IN EVERY CELL**

Aerobic Respiration *Needs Plenty of Oxygen*

1) <u>Aerobic respiration</u> is what happens when there's <u>plenty of oxygen</u> available.

2) "<u>Aerobic</u>" just means "<u>with oxygen</u>" and it's the most efficient way to release <u>energy</u> from <u>glucose</u>.

3) This is the type of respiration that you're using <u>most of the time</u>.

You need to learn <u>the word equation</u> and <u>the chemical equation</u>:

> Glucose + Oxygen $\longrightarrow$ Carbon dioxide + Water (+ Energy)
>
> $C_6H_{12}O_6 + 6O_2 \longrightarrow 6CO_2 + 6H_2O$ (+ Energy)

Anaerobic Respiration *Doesn't Use Oxygen At All*

1) When you do really <u>vigorous exercise</u> your body can't supply enough <u>oxygen</u> to your muscles for aerobic respiration — even though your <u>heart rate</u> and <u>breathing rate</u> increase as much as they can. Your muscles have to start <u>respiring anaerobically</u> as well.

2) "<u>Anaerobic</u>" just means "<u>without</u> oxygen". It's <u>NOT</u> the best way to convert glucose into energy because it releases much <u>less energy</u> than aerobic respiration. In anaerobic respiration, the glucose is only <u>partially</u> broken down, and <u>lactic acid</u> is also produced.

You need to learn <u>the word equation</u>: > Glucose $\longrightarrow$ Lactic Acid (+ Energy)

3) The <u>lactic acid</u> builds up in the muscles, which gets <u>painful</u> and makes your <u>muscles fatigued</u>.

4) The <u>advantage</u> is that at least you can keep on using your muscles.

5) After resorting to anaerobic respiration, when you stop exercising you'll have an <u>oxygen debt</u>.

6) Basically your muscles are <u>still short of oxygen</u> because they haven't been getting enough for a while. You also need <u>extra oxygen</u> to break down all the lactic acid that's built up in your muscles.

7) This means you have to keep <u>breathing hard</u> for a while <u>after you stop</u> exercising — to repay the debt.

8) The lactic acid has to be carried to the liver to be broken down, so your <u>heart rate</u> has to <u>stay high</u> too.

9) <u>Anaerobic respiration</u> does <u>not release nearly as much energy</u> as aerobic respiration — but it's useful in emergencies. <u>Unfit</u> people have to resort to <u>anaerobic</u> respiration <u>quicker</u> than fit people do.

I reckon aerobics classes should be called anaerobics instead...

OK, so when you're just sitting about, you use <u>aerobic respiration</u> to get all your energy — but when you do strenuous exercise, you can't get enough oxygen to your muscles, so you use <u>anaerobic respiration</u> too. Nothing too taxing here — just make sure you learn those equations.

Eating Healthily

As that doctor on the TV said this morning, food isn't just about energy — you need a balanced diet if you want to make sure that everything keeps working as it's supposed to.

A Balanced Diet Supplies All Your Essential Nutrients

A balanced diet gives you all the essential nutrients you need. The six essential nutrients are carbohydrates, proteins, fats, vitamins, minerals and water. You also need fibre (to keep the guts in good working order). Different nutrients are required for different functions in the body:

NUTRIENTS	FUNCTIONS
Carbohydrates	Carbohydrates (e.g. glucose) provide energy.
Fats	Fats provide energy, act as an energy store and provide insulation.
Proteins	Proteins are needed for growth and repair of tissue, and to provide energy in emergencies.
Vitamins	Various functions: e.g. vitamin C is needed to prevent scurvy.
Minerals	Various functions: e.g. iron is needed to make haemoglobin for healthy blood.
Water	We need a constant supply to replace water lost through urinating, breathing and sweating.

1) Carbohydrates are made up of simple sugars like glucose.
2) Fats are made up of fatty acids and glycerol.
3) Proteins are made up of amino acids.
Some amino acids can't be made by the body, so you have to get them from your diet — these are called essential amino acids. You can get all the essential amino acids by eating protein that comes from animals (in other words, meat). These animal proteins are called first class proteins. Vegetarians have to eat a varied diet to get all the essential amino acids they need.

Energy and Nutrient Needs Vary Between People

A balanced diet isn't a set thing — it's different for everyone. The balance of the different nutrients a person needs depends on things like their age, gender and activity level.

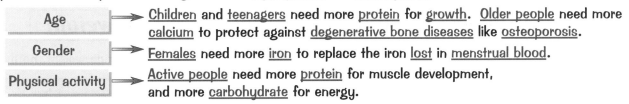

Age	→	Children and teenagers need more protein for growth. Older people need more calcium to protect against degenerative bone diseases like osteoporosis.
Gender	→	Females need more iron to replace the iron lost in menstrual blood.
Physical activity	→	Active people need more protein for muscle development, and more carbohydrate for energy.

Some People Choose to Eat a Different Diet

Some people choose not to eat some foods for all sorts of reasons:

1) Religious reasons — e.g. Hindus don't eat cows because they believe they're sacred.

2) Personal reasons — vegetarians don't eat meat for various reasons — some think it's cruel to animals, some don't like the taste and others think it's healthier not to eat it. Vegans don't eat any products from animals, e.g. milk, eggs and cheese.

3) Medical reasons — some people are intolerant to certain foods, e.g. dairy products or wheat. Eating them can make the person feel bloated and ill. This is often because they can't make the enzyme needed to digest that food properly. Some people are allergic to foods (nut allergies are quite common) — they get a severe reaction which can sometimes even be fatal.

I think the problem is that I've got an allergy to sprouts...

Having a food allergy can be a real pain. Just think how many random products have 'May contain nuts' on them. Some people carry a syringe of adrenaline to inject themselves with, just in case.

Diet Problems

You are what you eat, apparently. That makes me baked beans. But at least I'm not toast.

Eating Too Much Can Lead to Obesity

Some people have dietary disorders caused by too much food.

1) Obesity is a common disorder — it's defined as being 20% (or more) over recommended body weight.

2) Too much sugary or fatty food and too little exercise are the main causes of obesity.

3) People can also be obese due to an underactive thyroid gland, but this problem isn't common.

4) Obesity can increase the risk of diabetes, arthritis, high blood pressure, coronary heart disease (CHD) and even some forms of cancer, e.g. breast cancer.

Eating Too Little Can Also Cause Problems

1) Eating too little protein can cause a condition called kwashiorkor. A common symptom is a swollen stomach. Diets in many parts of the world are deficient in protein, especially in poorer developing countries — protein-rich foods are often too expensive to buy. Also, children need a greater proportion of protein than adults (so they can grow), so they may be more likely to suffer.

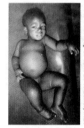
Photo courtesy of Tom D. Thacher, MD.
A kwashiorkor sufferer

You can calculate the recommended daily allowance (RDA) of protein using this formula:

$$\text{RDA (g)} = 0.75 \times \text{body mass (kg)}$$

2) Some psychological disorders cause under-nutrition, e.g. anorexia nervosa and bulimia nervosa. Anorexia nervosa leads to self-starvation. Bulimia nervosa involves bouts of binge eating, followed by self-induced vomiting. They're both usually caused by low self-esteem and anxiety about body fat — sufferers have a poor self-image. Even though sufferers may become very underweight, they still want to be thinner. These disorders cause a host of other illnesses, e.g. liver failure, kidney failure, heart attacks, muscle wastage, low blood pressure and mineral deficiencies. Bulimia can lead to tooth decay (the acid in vomit eats away at the tooth enamel). Both disorders can be fatal.

Body Mass Index Indicates If You're Under- or Overweight

The body mass index (BMI) is used as a guide to help decide whether someone is underweight, normal, overweight or obese. It's calculated from their height and weight:

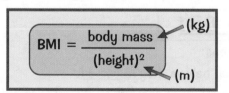
$$\text{BMI} = \frac{\text{body mass}}{(\text{height})^2} \quad \text{(kg)} \atop \text{(m)}$$

The table shows how BMI is used to classify people's weight.

Body Mass Index	Weight Description
below 18.5	underweight
18.5 - 24.9	normal
25 - 29.9	overweight
30 - 40	moderately obese
above 40	severely obese

BMI isn't always reliable. Athletes have lots of muscle, which weighs more than fat, so they can come out with a high BMI even though they're not overweight. An alternative to BMI is measuring % body fat.

Too much or too little — it's a fine line to tread...

Your health can really suffer if you regularly eat too much, too little, or miss out on a vital nutrient. Sometimes it seems like the whole world's obsessed with diets — there's a new miracle one every week. Don't believe everything you read though. Even if a celebrity swears by it, it doesn't mean it works.

Digestion

Digestion is the breaking down of the nutrients in your food, so that they can be absorbed.

Big Molecules are Broken Down into Smaller Ones

1) The aim of the game is to get all the nutrients from your food into your blood.

2) First the big lumps of food are physically digested so they can pass easily through the digestive system. This basically means chewing it in the mouth and churning it about in the stomach.

3) Then you use chemical digestion to break down molecules that are too big to pass through cell membranes.

4) This involves using enzymes — biological catalysts that break down the big molecules into smaller ones.

There are Three Main Types of Digestive Enzyme

1) CARBOHYDRASES break down big carbohydrates (e.g. STARCH) into SIMPLE SUGARS.
   They're present in two places:
   1) The mouth
   2) The small intestine

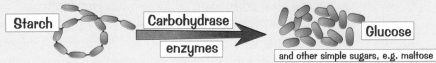

2) PROTEASES convert PROTEINS into AMINO ACIDS.
   They're present in two places:
   1) The stomach (where it's called pepsin)
   2) The small intestine

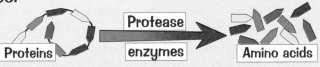

3) LIPASES convert FATS into FATTY ACIDS and GLYCEROL.
   They're present in the small intestine.

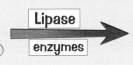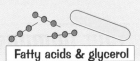

Other chemicals are also present in your body and help enzymes work effectively...

1) Stomach acid lowers the pH in the stomach, giving the right conditions for the digestive enzymes to work.

2) Bile is made in the liver and stored in the gall bladder. It helps digestion in the small intestine in two ways:
   • Bile is alkaline. It neutralises the acid from the stomach to make conditions right for the enzymes in the small intestine to work.
   • It also emulsifies fats. In other words it breaks the fat into tiny droplets. This gives a much bigger surface area of fat for the lipase enzymes to work on.

The Small Molecules Can Then Diffuse into the Blood

① Glucose and amino acids are small enough to diffuse into the blood plasma.

The products of fat digestion can't get into the blood plasma so they diffuse out of the gut (intestines) and into a fluid called lymph, in the lymphatic system. From here they're emptied into the blood.

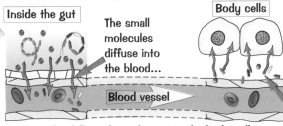

Blood flows from the gut to the body cells.

② The nutrients then travel to where they're needed, and then diffuse out again, e.g. glucose travels to muscles for respiration during exercise. It's all clever stuff.

Now get digesting those facts...

Revision is a lot like digestion if you think about it — you break down the big topics into manageable chunks and then absorb the information. Imagine if you could eat this book and absorb all the facts in one sitting... it'd make life easier. But getting back to the real world... a mini-essay or two will help.

Infectious Disease

There really are loads of things out to get you, and you really do have to fight attacks off every day.

Infectious Diseases are Caused by Pathogens

Pathogens are micro-organisms that cause disease. There are four types:

1) fungi — e.g. athlete's foot is caused by fungi
2) bacteria — e.g. cholera is caused by bacteria
3) viruses — e.g. flu is caused by a virus
4) protozoa (single-celled organisms) — e.g. dysentery can be caused by protozoa.

The symptoms of an infectious disease are caused by cell damage or by toxins produced by the pathogens.

Malaria is an Example of an Infectious Disease

1) Malaria is caused by a protozoan. It's carried by mosquitoes, which are insects that feed on the blood of animals (including humans).
2) The protozoan is a parasite (see page 27) and the animal it infects is called a host.
3) The mosquitoes are vectors, meaning they carry the disease without getting it themselves. They pick up the malarial parasite when they feed on an infected animal. Every time the mosquito feeds on another animal it infects it by inserting the parasite into the animal's blood vessels.
4) We know that mozzies carry malaria so we can target them to reduce the spread of infection:
   • The areas of water where mosquitoes lay their eggs can be drained or sprayed with insecticides.
   • Fish can be introduced into the water to eat mosquito larvae.
   • People can be protected from mosquitoes using insecticides and mosquito nets.

Your Immune System Deals with Pathogens

Once micro-organisms have entered your body they'll reproduce rapidly unless they're destroyed. That's the job of your immune system, and white blood cells are the most important part of it.

White blood cells travel around in your blood and crawl into every part of you, constantly patrolling for micro-organisms. When they come across an invading micro-organism they have three lines of attack:

1) Consuming Them

White blood cells can engulf foreign cells and digest them.

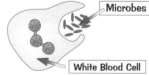

Microbes

White Blood Cell

2) Producing Antitoxins

Antitoxins counter the effect of any poisons (toxins) produced by the invading bacteria.

3) Producing Antibodies

1) Every pathogen has unique molecules on the surface of its cells — no two species have the same ones. These molecules are called antigens.
2) When your white blood cells come across a foreign antigen (like those on the surface of a bacterium) they'll start to produce proteins called antibodies, which lock on to and kill the new invading cells. The antibodies produced are specific to that pathogen — they won't lock on to other pathogens.
3) Antibodies are then produced rapidly and flow all round the body to kill all similar bacteria or viruses.
4) If the person is infected with the same pathogen again the white blood cells will quickly produce the antibodies to kill it — the person is naturally immune to that pathogen and won't get ill.

If athletes get athlete's foot — do vicars get dog-cholera...?

White blood cells aren't the body's only defence. Your skin provides a tough layer that stops most pathogens getting in to begin with, and if you get a cut in it, clotting quickly seals it up again. Most pathogens that get in through the mouth are killed by the acid in the stomach, or if they head towards the lungs they usually get stuck in the mucus produced by the cells lining your airways. Clever stuff.

Preventing and Treating Infectious Disease

An ounce of prevention is worth a pound of cure. That's what my mum says, anyhow.

Immunisation Stops You Getting Infections

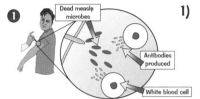

1) When you're infected with a <u>new</u> micro-organism it can take your white blood cells a while to produce the antibodies to deal with them. In that time you can get <u>very ill</u>, or maybe even die.

2) To avoid this you can be <u>immunised</u> against some diseases, e.g. polio or measles.

3) Immunisation involves injecting <u>dead or inactive</u> micro-organisms into the body. These carry <u>antigens</u>, so even though they're <u>harmless</u> your body makes <u>antibodies</u> to attack them.

4) If <u>live</u> micro-organisms of the <u>same type</u> appear after that, they'll be <u>killed immediately</u> by the antibodies which you've already developed against them. Cool.

Immunisation is classed as <u>active immunity</u>:

- <u>Active</u> immunity is where the immune system <u>makes its own antibodies</u> after being stimulated by a pathogen. It includes becoming <u>naturally immune</u> (see p.6) and <u>artificially immune</u> (<u>immunisation</u>). Active immunity is usually <u>permanent</u>.

- <u>Passive</u> immunity is where you use <u>antibodies made by another organism</u>, e.g. antibodies are passed from mother to baby through breast milk. Passive immunity is only <u>temporary</u>.

There are Benefits and Risks Associated with Immunisation

1) Immunisation <u>stops you from getting ill</u>... a pretty obvious benefit.

2) And if <u>most people</u> are immunised the disease won't be able to <u>spread</u> as easily.

3) But there can be <u>short-term side effects</u>, e.g. <u>swelling</u> and <u>redness</u> at the site of injection and feeling a bit <u>under the weather</u> for a week or two afterwards.

4) You can't have some vaccines if you're <u>already ill</u>, especially if your immune system is weakened.

5) Some people think that immunisation can <u>cause other disorders</u>, e.g. one study <u>suggested</u> a link between the <u>MMR</u> (measles, mumps and rubella) vaccine and <u>autism</u>. Most scientists say it's perfectly safe, but a lot of parents aren't willing to take the risk. This has led to a big rise in the number of children catching measles, and some people are now worried about an epidemic.

You Can Take Antibiotics to Get Rid of Bacterial Infections

1) <u>Antibiotics</u> are drugs that kill <u>bacteria</u> and <u>fungi</u> without killing your own body cells.

2) They're very useful for clearing up infections that your body is having <u>trouble</u> with.

3) However, they <u>don't kill viruses</u>. <u>Flu and colds</u> are caused by <u>viruses</u> and basically you just have to <u>wait</u> for your body to deal with them and <u>suffer</u> in the meantime.

A horrid Flu Virus

4) Some bacteria are naturally resistant to certain antibiotics. This is why you should always finish a course of antibiotics once you've started — to kill all the susceptible bacteria and give your immune system the best chance of killing off any antibiotic resistant bacteria left. Otherwise you risk leaving the resistant ones to thrive and multiply (and get <u>passed on</u> to other people).

<u>MRSA</u> (the hospital 'superbug' that people have been so worried about) is the best-known example of an antibiotic-resistant strain.

GCSEs are like antibiotics — you have to finish the course...

Science isn't just about doing an experiment, finding the answer and telling everyone about it — scientists often disagree. Not that long ago different scientists had different opinions on the <u>MMR</u> vaccine — and argued about its safety. Many different studies were done before scientists concluded it was safe.

Other Health Conditions

Disease and health disorders are when your health is impaired or your body functions abnormally. If you've ever thought you might be a hypochondriac, this page may not do you any favours.

Health Disorders Can be Caused in Various Ways

1) Vitamin deficiency, e.g. you can get scurvy if you don't get enough vitamin C.

2) Mineral deficiency, e.g. a lack of iron in the diet can lead to anaemia. Iron is needed to make the protein haemoglobin (which carries oxygen in the red blood cells).

3) Genetic inheritance of disorders (see p.19), e.g. red-green colour blindness (sufferers find it hard to distinguish between red and green) and haemophilia (a blood clotting disorder).

4) Body disorders are caused by body cells not working properly, e.g. diabetes (see p.14) and cancer.

> **Cancer is caused by body cells growing out of control**
>
> This forms a tumour (a mass of cells). Tumours can either be benign or malignant:
>
> 1) Benign — This is where the tumour grows until there's no more room. The cells stay where they are. This type isn't normally dangerous.
>
> 2) Malignant — This is where the tumour grows and can spread to other sites in the body. Malignant tumours are dangerous and can be fatal.
>
> Having a healthy lifestyle and diet can reduce your risk of getting some cancers:
>
> 1) Not smoking reduces your chances of getting lung cancer.
>
> 2) Wearing suncream when you go out in the Sun helps protect you against skin cancer.
>
> Different types of cancer have different survival rates, e.g. 77% of patients diagnosed with breast cancer survive for at least 5 years, whereas only 6% of lung cancer patients do.

Drugs Developed to Treat Disease Need to be Tested

New drugs developed to treat any kind of disease need to be thoroughly tested before they can be used. This is the usual way that drugs are developed and tested:

Computer models are often used first of all — these simulate a human's response to a drug, so you don't need to test on live animals at this stage. They can identify promising drugs to be tested in the next stage, but it's not as accurate as actually seeing the effect on a live organism.	The drugs are then developed further by testing on human tissues. However, you can't use human tissue to test drugs that affect whole/multiple body systems, e.g. testing a drug for blood pressure must be done on a whole animal, i.e. one that has an intact circulatory system.	The last step is to develop and test the drug using animals. The law in Britain states that any new drug must be tested on two different live mammals. Some people think it's cruel to test on animals, but others believe this is the safest way to make sure a drug isn't dangerous before it's given to humans.

After the drug has been tested on animals it's tested on humans:

1) This is done in a study called a clinical trial.

2) There are two groups of patients. One is given the new drug, the other is given a placebo (a 'sugar pill' that looks like the real drug but doesn't do anything). This is done so scientists can see the actual difference the drug makes — it allows for the placebo effect (when the patient expects the treatment to work and so feels better, even though the treatment isn't doing anything).

3) Clinical trials are blind — the patient in the study doesn't know whether they're getting the drug or the placebo. In fact, they're often double blind — neither the patient nor the scientist knows until all the results have been gathered.

Double Blindman's Buff — now that's got to be fun...

In the exam they might give you data relating to the survival or mortality (death) rates of different types of cancer and ask you to interpret it. Shouldn't be a problem if you can read a graph.

Drugs: Use and Harm

Drugs (both the legal kind and the illegal kind) might be in the exam. So get reading.

Drugs Can be Beneficial or Harmful

1) Drugs are substances which alter the way the body works. Some drugs are medically useful, such as antibiotics (e.g. penicillin). But many drugs are dangerous if misused.

2) This is why you can buy some drugs over the counter at a pharmacy, but others are restricted so you can only get them on prescription — your doctor decides if you should have them.

3) Some people get addicted to drugs — this means they have a physical need for the drug, and if they don't get it they get withdrawal symptoms. It's not just illegal drugs that are addictive — many legal ones are as well, e.g. caffeine in coffee. Caffeine withdrawal symptoms include irritability and shaky hands.

4) Tolerance develops with some drugs — the body gets used to having it and so you need a higher dose to give the same effect. This can happen with both legal drugs (e.g. alcohol), and illegal drugs (e.g. heroin).

5) If someone's addicted to a drug but wants to get off it, rehabilitation can help — this is where you get help and support to try and overcome an addiction.

You need to know all about these drugs...

1) Depressants — e.g. alcohol and temazepam. These decrease the activity of the brain. How they work is a bit complicated — they actually stimulate an area of the brain that decreases the activity of other parts. This slows down the responses of the nervous system, causing slow reactions and poor judgement of speed and distances (which is why drink driving is dangerous).

2) Stimulants — e.g. nicotine, ecstasy, caffeine. These do the opposite of depressants — they increase the activity of the brain, by increasing the amount of transmitter substance at some neurone synapses (p12). This makes you feel more alert and awake. Stimulant drugs are often used to treat depression.

3) Painkillers — e.g. aspirin. Aspirin is a mild painkiller that works by reducing the number of 'painful' stimuli at the nerve endings near an injury. Local anaesthetics are a different kind of painkiller — the painful stimuli still happen, but the nerve impulses are blocked.

4) Performance enhancers — e.g. anabolic steroids (testosterone, for example). These are sometimes taken by athletes. They help build muscle and allow the athletes to train harder. But they're banned by most sports organisations.

5) Hallucinogens — e.g. cannabis and LSD. They distort what's seen and heard by altering the pathways nerve impulses normally travel along.

Some Drugs are Illegal

1) In the UK, illegal drugs are classified into three main categories — Classes A, B and C. Which class a drug is in depends on how dangerous it is — Class A drugs are the most dangerous.

  • CLASS A drugs include heroin, LSD, ecstasy and cocaine.
  • CLASS B drugs include cannabis and amphetamines (speed).
  • CLASS C drugs include anabolic steroids and tranquillisers.

2) Using or dealing Class A drugs is most serious — you could get a lengthy prison sentence. Being caught with Class C drugs will probably only get you a warning, although prison's still a possibility.

3) In all cases, supplying a drug to others usually results in a greater punishment than just using it yourself.

4) Your school will have a policy about what to do if drug use is discovered. Different classes of drug may be treated differently — but whatever the class, the police will probably be informed. Usually, if someone's caught using drugs they'll be offered help to 'kick the habit'.

Drugs — they can cure you or kill you...

Many people take drugs of some kind, e.g. caffeine in coffee, headache tablets, alcohol, hayfever medicine or an inhaler for asthma. Most of these are okay if you're careful with them and don't go mad. It's misuse that can get you into trouble (e.g. a paracetamol overdose can kill you). Read the packet.

Smoking and Alcohol

Everyone knows that smoking doesn't do you much good. Unfortunately, it's unlikely that your exam question will ask whether smoking is good or bad for you — that's just not the way these things go. It's the details they'll want you to know. All those fiddly little tricky-to-learn details.

Alcohol is a Depressant Drug

1) Alcohol's main effect is to reduce the activity of the nervous system — it's a depressant (see p.9).

2) The positive side of this is that it makes people feel less inhibited. (Many people think that alcohol in moderation helps people to socialise and relax with each other.)

3) However, alcohol is poisonous. Normally, the liver breaks down the toxic alcohol into harmless by-products. But drinking too much too often causes death of liver cells, forming scar tissue that stops blood reaching the liver — this is called cirrhosis. If the liver can't do its normal job of cleaning the blood, dangerous substances start to build up and damage the rest of the body.

4) Alcohol also causes dehydration, which can damage other cells in the body (including in the brain).

5) Being drunk leads to impaired judgement, poor balance, poor coordination, slurred speech, blurred vision and sleepiness. This is why you're not allowed to drive, fly a plane or operate heavy machinery when you're drunk.

> There are legal alcohol limits...
> For driving in the UK it's 80 milligrams of alcohol in 100 millilitres of blood.
> For pilots it's 20 milligrams of alcohol per 100 millilitres of blood.

> And there are also 'lifestyle guidelines'...
> Doctors recommend drinking no more each week than 21 'units' of alcohol for a man, and 14 for a woman, where 1 unit is:
> (i) half a pint of average strength beer,
> (ii) 1 small glass of wine,
> (iii) 1 standard pub measure of spirits, etc.

Burning Cigarettes Produce Four Main Things:

1) CARBON MONOXIDE — This stops haemoglobin carrying as much oxygen. In pregnant women it deprives the foetus of oxygen leading to a small baby at birth.

2) NICOTINE — This is a stimulant drug and is what makes smoking addictive.

3) TAR — This covers the cilia (the little hairs in the respiratory tract), preventing them from moving bacteria and mucus out of your lungs (see below). It also contains carcinogens (see below).

4) PARTICULATES — These accumulate in the lung tissue, causing irritation.

Smoking Causes All Sorts of Illnesses

1) It causes disease of the heart and blood vessels, leading to heart attacks and strokes.

2) It causes lung, throat, mouth and oesophageal cancer:

> Tar from cigarette smoke collects in the lungs. It's full of toxic chemicals, some of which are carcinogens (cause cancer). Carcinogens make mutations in the DNA more likely. If this happens, cell division can go out of control and malignant tumours (see p.8) can form.

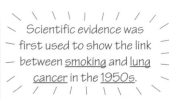
Scientific evidence was first used to show the link between smoking and lung cancer in the 1950s.

3) It causes severe loss of lung function, leading to diseases like emphysema and bronchitis:

> Smoking destroys the cilia on the epithelial tissue lining the trachea (windpipe). It also irritates the bronchi and bronchioles (in the lungs), which encourages mucus to be produced. But excess mucus can't be cleared properly because the cilia are damaged, so it sticks to air passages causing smoker's cough and chronic bronchitis. The lungs also lose their elasticity, causing emphysema.

The tar in cigarettes makes cilia black...

In the exam you might be asked to interpret data on the effects of smoking or alcohol, e.g. birth weights of babies born to mothers who smoke compared to those who don't, or the link between reaction time and alcohol level, etc. Don't panic — they'll give you any information you need to answer the question.

Receptors — The Eye

Your body has <u>sense organs</u> containing <u>receptors</u> that gather information about the world around you. The <u>skin</u> is sensitive to <u>pressure</u> and <u>temperature</u> and is responsible for the sense of <u>touch</u>. The <u>tongue</u> responds to <u>chemicals</u> in food (<u>taste</u>), the <u>nose</u> to <u>chemicals</u> in air (<u>smell</u>) and the <u>ears</u> to <u>sound</u> (<u>hearing</u>). But my own personal favourite is the <u>eye</u>, which is sensitive to <u>light</u> and is responsible for <u>sight</u>.

Learn the Eye with All Its Labels:

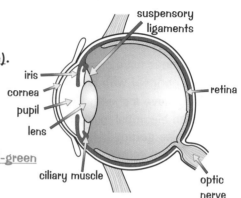

1) The <u>cornea refracts</u> (bends) light into the eye.
2) The <u>iris</u> controls <u>how much light</u> enters the <u>pupil</u> (<u>hole</u> in the <u>middle</u>).
3) The <u>lens focuses</u> the <u>light</u> onto the <u>retina</u>.
4) The <u>retina</u> is the <u>light sensitive</u> part and it's covered in receptors called <u>rods</u> and <u>cones</u>, which detect light.
5) <u>Rods</u> are more sensitive in <u>dim light</u> but <u>can't</u> sense colour.
6) <u>Cones</u> are sensitive to <u>colours</u> but are not so good in dim light (<u>red-green colour blindness</u> (see p.19) is due to a <u>lack</u> of certain <u>cone cells</u>).
7) The <u>optic nerve</u> carries impulses from the receptors to the <u>brain</u>.

Focusing on Near and Distant Objects

The eye focuses light by <u>changing</u> the <u>shape</u> of the <u>lens</u> — this is known as <u>accommodation</u>.

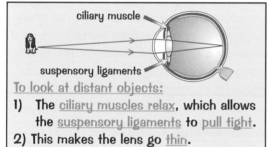

<u>To look at distant objects:</u>
1) The <u>ciliary muscles relax</u>, which allows the <u>suspensory ligaments</u> to <u>pull tight</u>.
2) This makes the lens go <u>thin</u>.

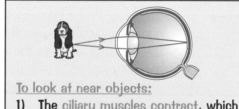

<u>To look at near objects:</u>
1) The <u>ciliary muscles contract</u>, which <u>slackens</u> the <u>suspensory ligaments</u>.
2) The lens becomes <u>fat</u>.

As you get older, your eye's <u>lens</u> loses <u>flexibility</u>, so it can't easily spring back to a round shape. This means light can't be <u>focused</u> well for near viewing, so older people often have to use reading glasses.

Some People are Long- or Short-sighted

<u>Long-sighted</u> people are <u>unable to focus</u> on <u>near</u> objects:
1) This occurs when the <u>cornea</u> or <u>lens</u> doesn't <u>bend</u> the light enough or the <u>eyeball</u> is too <u>short</u>.
2) The images of near objects are brought into focus <u>behind</u> the <u>retina</u>.
3) You can use glasses or contact lenses with a <u>convex lens</u> to correct it.

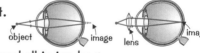

<u>Short-sighted</u> people are <u>unable to focus</u> on <u>distant</u> objects:
1) This occurs when the <u>cornea</u> or <u>lens</u> bends the light <u>too much</u> or the <u>eyeball</u> is too <u>long</u>.
2) The images of distant objects are brought into focus <u>in front</u> of the <u>retina</u>.
3) You can use glasses or contact lenses with a <u>concave lens</u> to correct it.

An alternative to glasses or contact lenses is to have <u>cornea laser surgery</u>.

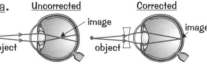

Binocular Vision Lets You Judge Depth

1) Some animals, including humans, have two eyes which <u>work together</u> — this is <u>binocular vision</u>. The brain uses small differences between what each eye sees to <u>judge distances</u> and <u>how fast</u> things are moving. It's handy for <u>catching prey</u> and deciding if it's safe to cross a road.
2) Other animals, like turkeys and lizards, have <u>monocular vision</u>. Their eyes see <u>totally separate views</u>, meaning they have a <u>wider field of vision</u>, but can't easily judge depth or speed. The advantage of <u>monocular</u> vision is that the organisms are more likely to <u>notice predators</u>.

I think I'm a little long-sighted...

If you can read this you've got better eyesight than me!

To see how important <u>binocular vision</u> is, cover one eye and try pouring water into a glass at arm's length. That's why you never see turkeys or lizards pouring themselves a glass of orange squash.

Neurones and Reflexes

All that information you gather with your eyes (and all your other senses) needs to be transmitted to the central nervous system so you can decide what to do about it.

Neurones Transmit Information Around the Body

Neurones (nerve cells) transmit information as electrical impulses around the body.

1) The electrical impulse is passed along the axon of the cell.

2) Neurones have branched endings so they can connect with lots of other neurones.

3) They have a sheath along the axon that acts as an electrical insulator, which stops the impulse getting lost. It also speeds up the electrical impulse.

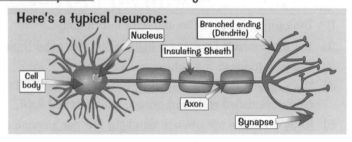

Here's a typical neurone:

4) They're long, which also speeds up the impulse (connecting with another neurone slows the impulse down, so one long neurone is much quicker than lots of short ones joined together).

5) The connection between two neurones is called a synapse. It's basically just a very tiny gap:

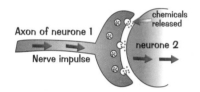

- The nerve signal is transferred by transmitter chemicals which diffuse across the gap.
- These chemicals then set off a new electrical impulse in the next neurone.
- Stimulant drugs increase the amount of transmitter chemical at some synapses, which increases the frequency of impulses along neurone 2.
- Depressants increase the amount of a different transmitter chemical at some synapses, which decreases the frequency of impulses set off along neurone 2. This decreases brain activity.

The Central Nervous System (CNS) Coordinates Information

1) The CNS consists of the brain and spinal cord (the peripheral nervous system is all the other neurones).

2) When you detect a change in your environment (a stimulus) your sensory neurones carry the information from receptors (e.g. light receptors in the back of the eye) to the CNS.

3) The CNS then sends information to an effector (muscle or gland) along a motor neurone. The effector then responds accordingly.

4) The job of the CNS is to COORDINATE the information.

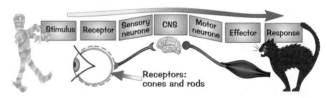

Receptors: cones and rods

Reflex Actions Stop You Injuring Yourself

1) The nervous system uses electrical impulses to allow very quick responses. Reflex actions are automatic (done without thinking) so they're even quicker.

2) The conscious brain isn't involved in a reflex arc. The sensory neurone joins to a relay neurone in the spinal cord (part of the CNS) — which links directly to the right motor neurone, so no time's wasted thinking about the right response.

3) Reflex actions often have a protective role, e.g. snatching back your hand when you touch a burning hot plate happens almost before you realise you've done it.

5. Message travels along a motor neurone

4. Message is passed along a relay neurone

6. When message reaches muscle, it contracts to move arm away from bee

CNS

3. Message travels along the sensory neurone

2. Stimulation of the pain receptor

1. Cheeky bee stings finger

Don't let the thought of exams play on your nerves...

Another example of a reflex is when the pupil in your eye constricts in bright light — it stops your eye getting damaged. Control of your posture happens automatically too — thanks to reflex arcs.

Homeostasis

Homeostasis involves balancing body functions to maintain a 'constant internal environment'. Smashing.

Homeostasis is Maintaining a Constant Internal Environment

Conditions in your body need to be kept steady so that cells can function properly. This involves balancing inputs (stuff going into your body) with outputs (stuff leaving). For example...

1) Levels of CO_2 — respiration (see p.2) constantly produces CO_2, which you need to get rid of.

2) Water content — you need to keep a balance between the water you gain (in drink, food, and from respiration) and the water you pee, sweat and breathe out.

3) Body temperature — you need to get rid of excess body heat when you're hot, but retain heat when the environment is cold.

A mechanism called negative feedback helps you keep all these things steady:

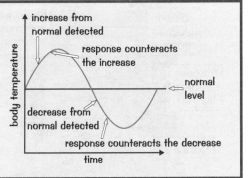

NEGATIVE FEEDBACK

Changes in the environment trigger a response that counteracts the changes — e.g. a rise in body temperature causes a response that lowers body temperature.

This means that the internal environment tends to stay around a norm, the level at which the cells work best.

This only works within certain limits — if the environment changes too much then it might not be possible to counteract it.

Body Temperature is Controlled by the Brain

All enzymes work best at a certain temperature. The enzymes in the human body work best at about 37 °C.

1) There's a thermoregulatory centre in the brain which acts as your own personal thermostat.

2) It contains receptors that are sensitive to the blood temperature in the brain. It also receives impulses from the skin that provide information about skin temperature.

To keep your enzymes at warm and toasty 37 °C your body does these things:

When You're TOO HOT:

1) Hairs lie flat.
2) Lots of sweat is produced — when it evaporates it transfers heat to the environment, cooling you down.
3) Blood vessels close to the surface of the skin widen. This allows more blood to flow near the surface, so it can radiate more heat into the surroundings. This is called vasodilation.

If you're exposed to high temperatures you can get dehydrated and you could get heat stroke. This can kill you (see below).

When You're TOO COLD:

1) Hairs stand on end to trap an insulating layer of air which helps keep you warm.
2) Very little sweat is produced.
3) Blood vessels near the surface constrict (vasoconstriction) so that less heat can be transferred from the blood to the surroundings.
4) You shiver, and the movement generates heat in the muscles.

Your body temperature can drop to dangerous levels if you're exposed to very low temperatures for a long time — this is called hypothermia. If you don't get help quickly you can die.

If you do enough revision, you can avoid negative feedback...

If you're in really high temperatures for a long time you can get heat stroke — sweating stops because you're so dehydrated and there's a big rise in your body temperature. Your enzymes can't work properly and important reactions get disrupted — if you don't cool down you could collapse and die. Fortunately, good old British drizzle means that heat stroke needn't worry the majority of us. Lucky old us.

Controlling Blood Sugar

Blood sugar is controlled as part of homeostasis, using the hormone insulin. Learn how it works.

Insulin Controls Blood Sugar Levels

1) Eating foods containing carbohydrate puts glucose into the blood from the gut.

2) Normal respiration (see p.2) in cells removes glucose from the blood.

3) Vigorous exercise also removes a lot of glucose from the blood.

4) Levels of glucose in the blood must be kept steady. Changes in blood glucose are monitored and controlled by the pancreas, using insulin...

Blood glucose level TOO HIGH — insulin is ADDED

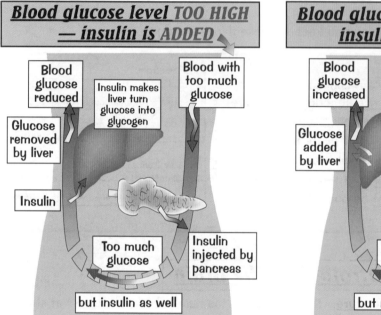

Blood glucose level TOO LOW — insulin is NOT ADDED

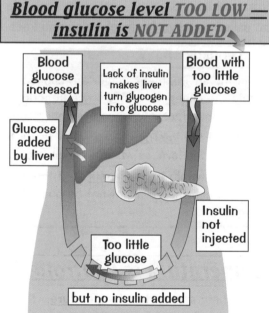

Glycogen can be stored in the liver until blood sugar levels get low again. Muscles have their own store.

Diabetes — the Pancreas Stops Making Enough Insulin

1) Diabetes (type 1) is a condition where the pancreas doesn't produce enough insulin.

2) The result is that a person's blood glucose level can rise to a level that can kill them.

3) The problem can be controlled in two ways:

   a) Avoiding foods rich in simple carbohydrates, i.e. sugars (which cause glucose levels to rise rapidly). It can also be helpful to take exercise after eating to try and use up the extra glucose produced during digestion — but this isn't usually very practical.

   b) Injecting insulin into the blood at mealtimes. This will make the liver remove the glucose as soon as it enters the blood from the gut, when the food is being digested. This stops the level of glucose in the blood from getting too high, and is a very effective treatment. However, diabetics must make sure they eat sensibly after injecting insulin, or their blood sugar could drop dangerously.

4) The amount of insulin that needs to be injected depends on the person's diet and how active they are.

5) Diabetics can check their blood sugar using a glucose-monitoring device. This is a little hand-held machine. They prick their finger to get a drop of blood for the machine to check.

My blood sugar feels low after all that — pass the biscuits...

This stuff can seem a bit confusing at first, but if you learn those two diagrams, it'll all start to get a lot easier. Don't forget that there are two ways to control diabetes — diet and injecting insulin.

Hormones

As well as blood sugar levels, hormones control everything to do with <u>sex</u> and <u>reproduction</u>.

Hormones ___Promote Sexual Characteristics at Puberty___

At puberty your body starts releasing <u>sex hormones</u> — <u>testosterone</u> in men and <u>oestrogen</u> in women. These trigger off the <u>secondary sexual characteristics</u>:

In men
1) <u>Extra hair</u> on face and body.
2) <u>Muscles develop</u>.
3) <u>Penis and testicles</u> enlarge.
4) <u>Sperm</u> production.
5) <u>Deepening</u> of <u>voice</u>.

In women
1) <u>Extra hair</u> on underarms and pubic area.
2) <u>Hips widen</u>.
3) Development of <u>breasts</u>.
4) <u>Egg</u> release and <u>periods start</u>.

Hormones ___Also Control the___ ___Menstrual Cycle___

Two hormones that are produced in the <u>ovaries</u> control the main events of the cycle:

| 1) Oestrogen: | 1) Causes the <u>lining</u> of the <u>uterus</u> to <u>thicken</u> ready for a fertilised egg to implant. |
| | 2) Stimulates the <u>release of an egg</u> at day 14. |

| 2) Progesterone: | <u>Maintains</u> the lining of the uterus. |
| | When the level of progesterone <u>falls</u>, the lining <u>breaks down</u>. |

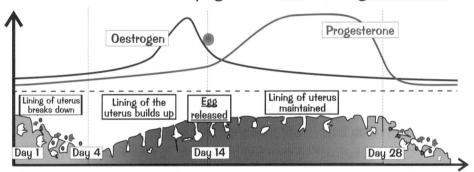

Oestrogen ___and___ *Progesterone* ___are Used in___ ___Contraception___

1) "<u>The Pill</u>", as it's cheerfully known, contains both <u>progesterone</u> and <u>oestrogen</u>.

2) It may seem kind of strange, but even though oestrogen stimulates the <u>release</u> of eggs, if it's taken <u>every day</u> so that its levels are <u>permanently high</u> it eventually <u>stops</u> egg release. This is because it <u>inhibits</u> the production of another female sex hormone, <u>FSH</u>. This <u>mimics pregnancy</u> — when a woman is pregnant her <u>oestrogen</u> levels remain <u>high</u> all the time, and she doesn't release any eggs.

3) There is also a <u>progesterone only pill</u> (no oestrogen) which works by stimulating the production of <u>thick cervical mucus</u> which prevents any sperm getting through and reaching an egg. If one does manage to sneak through, the high progesterone levels also help stop fertilised eggs <u>implanting</u> in the uterus.

FSH is Used to Stimulate Egg Production ___in Fertility Treatment___

1) <u>FSH</u> can be taken by women who <u>aren't releasing eggs</u> to stimulate <u>egg development</u> in their ovaries.

2) FSH stimulates the ovaries to produce <u>oestrogen</u>, which in turn stimulates the <u>release</u> of an <u>egg</u>.

3) But you do have to be <u>careful</u> with the <u>dosage</u> or you get too many eggs being released. This can result in <u>multiple births</u> (twins, triplets and so on) which can be more <u>risky</u> for the mum and the babies.

What do you call a fish with no eye... FSH...

Places where hormones are produced, like the pancreas, ovaries and testes, are known as <u>endocrine glands</u>. They release the hormone into the <u>blood</u>, and it travels all around the body until it reaches its <u>target cells</u>. This makes hormonal reactions <u>slower</u> than nervous reactions, which are more <u>direct</u>.

Genes and Chromosomes

If you're going to get <u>anywhere</u> with this topic you have to make sure you know <u>exactly</u> what <u>DNA</u> is, what and where <u>chromosomes</u> are, and what and where a <u>gene</u> is. If you don't get that sorted out first, then anything else you read about them won't make a lot of sense to you.

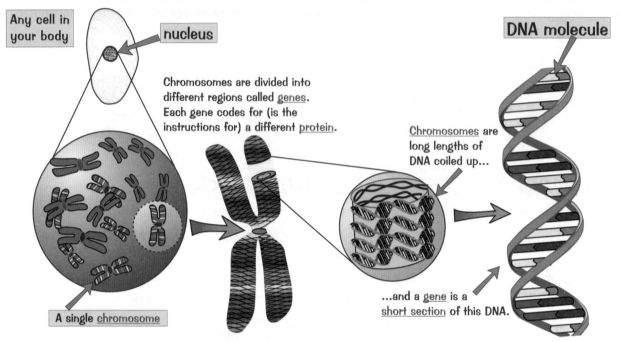

Any cell in your body

nucleus

DNA molecule

Chromosomes are divided into different regions called <u>genes</u>. Each gene codes for (is the instructions for) a different <u>protein</u>.

Chromosomes are long lengths of DNA coiled up...

A single <u>chromosome</u>

...and a <u>gene</u> is a <u>short section</u> of this DNA.

The human cell nucleus contains <u>46 chromosomes</u> arranged in <u>23 pairs</u>.
They're all well known and numbered — you have two number 19 chromosomes,
two number 12s and so on. (Other species have <u>different</u> numbers of chromosomes in their cells.)

Genes <u>are</u> Chemical Instructions

1) DNA is a long list of <u>instructions</u> on how to put an organism together and <u>make it work</u>.

2) Each <u>separate gene</u> is a <u>chemical instruction</u> showing how to make a particular <u>protein</u>.

3) Proteins are important because they <u>control</u> most <u>processes</u> in the body — <u>enzymes</u> are proteins, for example. Proteins also assemble everything that isn't a protein, e.g. they help build cell membranes.

4) Cells make <u>proteins</u> by stringing <u>amino acids</u> together in a particular order.
Genes simply tell cells the <u>correct order</u>.

> The DNA double helix is made up of two "<u>strands</u>" that are joined together by things called <u>bases</u>. There are <u>four</u> different kinds of base in DNA — <u>A</u>, <u>T</u>, <u>C</u> and <u>G</u>. The <u>order</u> of the bases in a gene controls the order of amino acids in a protein.
> <u>Each gene</u> contains a <u>different sequence</u> of these bases.

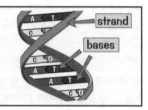

strand

bases

5) We only use about <u>20</u> different amino acids — since in different combinations these can make up <u>thousands</u> (well... in theory, billions) of different <u>proteins</u>.

The 'genetic code' describes how groups of bases are 'translated' into specific amino acids.

6) Genes control what proteins are made in a cell, and this determines what <u>type of cell</u> it is, e.g. white blood cell, skin cell, etc.

7) Not every gene is used to produce a protein in every cell — some genes are <u>switched off</u>. It depends on what type of cell it is and what it's doing at the time.

<u>Revision and proteins — just string things together...</u>

Humans have about <u>25 000 genes</u> in every single cell — and each gene makes a <u>different protein</u>... amazing really. Your genes control all sorts of things, like your blood type, eye colour, hair colour (unless you dye it of course) and whether you can roll your tongue (make it tube shaped) or not. Go on.. have a go.

Genetic Variation

Everyone (except identical twins) has <u>different genes</u> to everyone else. And here's why...

There are Two Sources of Genetic Variation

① Gamete Formation — Making Sperm Cells and Egg Cells...

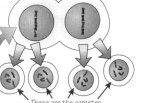

Reproductive cell with its pairs of chromosomes.

(Blue chromosomes are from mum.)
(Red chromosomes are from dad.)

1) Gametes are <u>sperm cells</u> and <u>egg cells</u>. Gametes are formed in the ovaries or testes from <u>reproductive cells</u>.

2) Reproductive cells (like all human body cells) have <u>23 pairs</u> of chromosomes. In each pair there's one chromosome that was <u>originally inherited</u> from <u>mum</u>, and one that was inherited from <u>dad</u>.

3) When reproductive cells <u>split</u> into two, some of your dad's chromosomes are grouped with some from your mum.

4) This shuffling up of chromosomes leads to <u>variation</u> in the new generation.

These are the gametes.

...then Fertilisation — the Gametes Join Together

Gametes

sperm + egg

fertilised egg

1) Fertilisation is when the <u>sperm</u> and the <u>egg</u>, with <u>23 chromosomes each</u>, join to form a new cell with the full <u>46 chromosomes</u>.

2) But (in nature, at least) fertilisation is a bit random — you don't know which two gametes are going to join together.

② Mutations — Changes to the Genetic Code

1) Occasionally a gene may <u>mutate</u>. Mutations usually <u>change the sequence</u> of the <u>DNA bases</u>. This could <u>stop the production</u> of a <u>protein</u>, or it might mean a <u>different</u> protein is produced instead. This can lead to <u>new characteristics</u>, <u>increasing variation</u>.

2) Mutations can happen <u>spontaneously</u> — when a chromosome doesn't quite copy itself properly. However, the chance of mutation is <u>increased</u> by exposing yourself to:
   - nuclear radiation, X-rays or ultraviolet light,
   - <u>chemicals</u> called <u>mutagens</u>. (Cigarette smoke contains <u>mutagens</u>.)
   If the mutations lead to cancer then the chemicals are called carcinogens.

No no! not me!

3) Mutations are usually harmful.
   - If a mutation occurs in <u>reproductive cells</u>, the offspring might develop <u>abnormally</u> or <u>die</u>.
   - If a mutation occurs in body cells, the mutant cells may start to <u>multiply</u> in an <u>uncontrolled</u> way and <u>invade</u> other parts of the body (which is <u>cancer</u>).

4) <u>Very occasionally</u>, mutations are beneficial and give an organism a survival <u>advantage</u>, so it can live on in conditions where the others die. This is <u>natural selection</u> at work.
   For example, a mutation in a bacterium might make it <u>resistant to antibiotics</u>. If this mutant gene is passed on, you might get a <u>resistant</u> "<u>strain</u>" of bacteria, which antibiotics can't kill.

Most features are determined by both your GENES and your ENVIRONMENT:

It's not just genes that determine how you turn out though. Your <u>environment</u> has a big effect too. For some characteristics, it's hard to say which factor is more important — genes or environment...

1) <u>Health</u> — Some people are more likely to get certain <u>diseases</u> (e.g. <u>cancer</u> and <u>heart disease</u>) because of their genes. But <u>lifestyle</u> also affects the risk, e.g. if you smoke or only eat junk food.

2) <u>Intelligence</u> — One theory is that although your <u>maximum possible IQ</u> might be determined by your <u>genes</u>, whether you get to it depends on your <u>environment</u>, e.g. your <u>upbringing</u> and <u>school</u> life.

3) <u>Sporting ability</u> — Again, genes probably determine your <u>potential</u>, but training is important too.

So if you weren't picked for netball — blame your parents...

So in <u>sexual reproduction</u> a mixture of chromosomes is randomly shuffled into <u>gametes</u>. Then a random gamete fuses with another random gamete at <u>fertilisation</u> (oh, the romance of it all).

Genetic Diagrams

In the exam they could ask about the inheritance of <u>any</u> kind of characteristic that's controlled by a <u>single</u> <u>gene</u>. Luckily, the basic idea's always the same, whatever the gene...

Genetic Diagrams *Show the Possible Genes of Offspring*

1) <u>Alleles</u> are <u>different versions</u> of the <u>same gene</u>.

2) Most of the time you have <u>two</u> of each gene (i.e. two alleles) — one from each parent.

3) If the alleles are different you have instructions for two different versions of a characteristic (e.g. blue eyes or brown eyes), but you only show one version of the two (e.g. brown eyes). The version of the characteristic that appears is caused by the <u>dominant allele</u>. The other allele is said to be <u>recessive</u>.

4) In genetic diagrams <u>letters</u> are used to represent <u>genes</u>. <u>Dominant</u> alleles are always shown with a <u>capital letter</u>, and <u>recessive</u> alleles with a <u>small letter</u>.

5) If you're <u>homozygous</u> for a trait you have <u>two alleles the same</u> for that particular gene, e.g. CC or cc. If you're <u>heterozygous</u> for a trait you have <u>two different alleles</u> for that particular gene, e.g. Cc.

You Need to be Able to Interpret, Explain and Construct Them

Imagine you're cross-breeding <u>hamsters</u>, and that some have a normal, boring disposition while others have a leaning towards crazy acrobatics. And suppose you know the behaviour is due to one gene...

Let's say that the allele which causes the crazy nature is <u>recessive</u> — so use a '<u>b</u>'.
And normal (boring) behaviour is due to a <u>dominant allele</u> — call it '<u>B</u>'.

1) For an organism to display a <u>recessive</u> characteristic, <u>both</u> its alleles must be <u>recessive</u> — so a crazy hamster must have the alleles 'bb' (i.e. it must be homozygous for this trait).

2) However, a <u>normal hamster</u> could be BB (homozygous) or Bb (heterozygous), because the dominant allele (B) <u>overrules</u> the recessive one (b).

So if you cross a <u>thoroughbred crazy hamster</u>, genetic type bb, with a <u>thoroughbred normal hamster</u>, BB, you get this...

Parents: normal and boring parent   crazy parent

Parents' alleles: (BB)   (bb)

Gametes' alleles: (B) (B) (b) (b)

Possible combinations of alleles in offspring: (Bb) (Bb) (Bb) (Bb)

They're <u>all</u> normal and boring.

The lines show <u>all</u> the <u>possible</u> ways the parents' alleles <u>could</u> combine.

Remember, only <u>one</u> of these possibilities would <u>actually happen</u> for any one offspring.

When you breed two organisms together to look at one characteristic it's called a MONOHYBRID CROSS.

If two of these <u>offspring</u> now breed they will produce a <u>new combination</u> of kids.

This time, there's a 75% chance of having a normal, boring hamster, and a 25% chance of a crazy one.

Parents: normal and boring   normal and boring

Parents' alleles: (Bb)   (Bb)

Gametes' alleles: (B) (b) (B) (b)

Possible combinations of alleles in offspring: (BB) (Bb) (Bb) (bb)

normal   normal   normal   <u>crazy!</u>

It's not just hamsters that have the wild and scratty allele...

...my sister definitely has it too. Remember, 'results' like this are only <u>probabilities</u>. It doesn't mean it'll actually happen. (Most likely, you'll end up trying to contain a mini-riot of nine lunatic baby hamsters.)

Genetic Diagrams and Disorders

Here's a few examples that you need to understand. But they're not hard. So stop looking so worried.

Your Chromosomes Control Whether You're Male or Female

There are 23 matched pairs of chromosomes in every human body cell. The 23rd pair are labelled XY. They're the two chromosomes that decide whether you turn out male or female.

All men have an X and a Y chromosome: XY The Y chromosome causes male characteristics.	All women have two X chromosomes: XX The XX combination causes female characteristics.

This is true for all mammals, but not for some other organisms, e.g. plants.

There's an Equal Chance of Having a Boy or a Girl...

...and there's a genetic diagram to prove it.

Even though we're talking about inheriting chromosomes here and not single genes, the genetic diagram still works the same way.

When you plug all the letters into the diagram, it shows that there are two XX results and two XY results, so there's the same probability of getting a boy or a girl.

Don't forget that this 50:50 ratio is only a probability. If you had four kids they could all be boys.

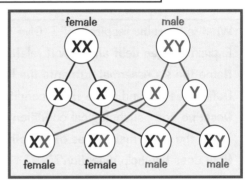

Cystic Fibrosis is Caused by a Recessive Allele

Defective alleles are responsible for genetic disorders. Most of these defective alleles are recessive.

Cystic fibrosis is a genetic disorder of the cell membranes. It results in the body producing a lot of thick sticky mucus in the air passages and in the pancreas.

1) The allele which causes cystic fibrosis is a recessive allele, 'f', carried by about 1 person in 25.

2) Because it's recessive, people with only one copy of the allele won't have the disorder — they're known as carriers.

3) For a child to have a chance of inheriting the disorder, both parents must be either carriers or sufferers.

4) As the diagram shows, there's a 1 in 4 chance of a child having the disorder if both parents are carriers.

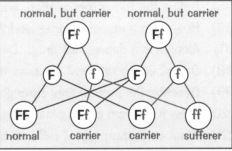

Knowing About Genetic Disorders Opens Up a Whole Can of Worms

Knowing there are inherited conditions in your family raises difficult issues:

• Should all family members be tested to see if they're carriers? Some people might prefer not to know, but is this fair on any partners or future children they might have?

• Is it right for someone who's at risk of passing on a genetic condition to have children? Is it fair to put them under pressure not to, if they decide they want children?

• It's possible to test a foetus for some genetic conditions while it's still in the womb. But if the test is positive, is it right to terminate the pregnancy? The family might not be able to cope with a sick or disabled child, but why should that child have a lesser right to life than a healthy child? Some people think abortion is always wrong under any circumstances.

What do you get when you cross a snowman with a vampire?

...frostbite. There are lots of other genetic disorders — e.g. red-green colour blindness and sickle cell anaemia. To work out the chance of any inherited disorders being passed on, follow the same method.

Revision Summary for Module B1

That was a long section, but kind of interesting, I reckon. These questions will show what you know and what you don't... if you get stuck, have a look back to remind yourself. But before the exam, make sure you can do all of them without any help — that's the only way you'll know you're ready.

1) What's the difference between 'fit' and 'healthy'? Can you be one without being the other?

2)* Below are the blood pressure measurements of a group of GCSE students and a group of teachers.

Group A	Person 1	Person 2	Person 3	Person 4	Person 5	Person 6
Systolic pressure (mm Hg)	126	100	110	110	114	112
Diastolic pressure (mm Hg)	84	72	60	78	66	68

Group B	Person 1	Person 2	Person 3	Person 4	Person 5	Person 6
Systolic pressure (mm Hg)	138	150	122	118	120	116
Diastolic pressure (mm Hg)	100	100	80	78	84	68

a) Is Group A likely to be teachers or students? Explain your answer.

b) How many of the teachers would be considered to have high blood pressure?

c) What would you advise these teachers to do to help reduce their blood pressure?

3) What is "aerobic respiration"? Give the word and symbol equations for it.

4) Explain oxygen debt and how it relates to fitness.

5) Name the six essential nutrients the body needs and what they are used for.

6) Define obesity and name three conditions obese people are at an increased risk of getting.

7) Describe one psychological condition that can cause under-nutrition.

8) Name the three main types of digestive enzyme and explain what they do.

9) How does bile help digestion?

10) Name the four types of micro-organism that cause disease, giving an example for each.

11) Explain how the immune system deals with pathogens.

12) Explain how immunisation stops you getting infections.

13) Explain the difference between benign and malignant tumours.

14) What is a double blind clinical trial?

15) Define the terms prescription, addiction, tolerance and rehabilitation.

16) How does a stimulant drug work? Give two examples.

17) Alcohol is a depressant drug. Describe the symptoms of too much alcohol.

18) Describe four different illnesses that smoking can cause.

19) Describe the path of light through the eye.

20) Draw a diagram of a typical neurone, labelling all its parts.

21) What is the purpose of reflex actions?

22) Explain how negative feedback helps to maintain a constant internal environment.

23) Describe how body temperature is reduced when you're too hot.

24) Explain how insulin controls blood sugar levels.

25) Define diabetes and explain two ways in which it can be controlled.

26) What secondary sexual characteristics does testosterone trigger in males?

27) How does the hormone FSH increase fertility in women?

28) Describe the structure of DNA. What are genes?

29) Explain how bases determine what protein a gene codes for.

30) Name two sources of genetic variation.

31) Name three things that cause genetic mutations.

32) What is an allele?

33)*Draw a genetic diagram for a cross between a man with blue eyes (bb) and a woman who has green eyes (Bb). The gene for blue eyes (b) is recessive.

34) Which chromosomes determine your gender? Draw a genetic diagram showing that there's an equal chance of a baby being a boy or a girl.

* Answers on p.108

Module B1 — Understanding Ourselves

Ecosystems

An <u>ecosystem</u> is all the <u>different organisms</u> living together in a <u>particular environment</u>. Sounds cosy.

Artificial Ecosystems **Can be** Carefully Controlled

1) There are <u>two types of ecosystem</u> you need to know about:

> A <u>NATURAL ECOSYSTEM</u> is one where humans <u>don't control the processes</u> going on within it.
> An <u>ARTIFICIAL ECOSYSTEM</u> is one where humans <u>deliberately</u> promote the growth of certain living organisms and get rid of others which threaten their well-being.

2) Humans <u>might</u> affect <u>natural ecosystems</u> in some way, but they <u>don't take deliberate steps</u> to decide what animals and plants should be there.

3) <u>Artificial ecosystems</u> are most common in money-making enterprises, e.g. <u>farms</u> and <u>market gardens</u>. A particular plant may be favoured by <u>planting</u> lots of it and <u>applying fertiliser</u>, or an animal may be <u>fed</u> and <u>cared for</u>. Other organisms that might cause problems are <u>reduced or got rid of</u> by the use of <u>weed killers</u> and <u>pesticides</u>.

4) This means that <u>artificial ecosystems</u> normally have a <u>smaller number of species</u> (less biodiversity) than natural ones.

Woodlands **and** Lakes **are** Natural Ecosystems

1) In most woodlands and lakes the natural community is largely <u>left alone</u> by humans and a large number of species live there <u>in balance</u>.

2) Sometimes humans <u>pollute</u> lakes, but this is not done on purpose to control the populations.

3) Many woodlands are 'managed' by humans to some extent. E.g. selected trees are felled so that light can reach ground plants, or the populations of animals that damage trees (like squirrels and deer) are controlled. In extreme cases, this can turn woodland into an <u>artificial ecosystem</u>.

Greenhouses **are** Artificial Ecosystems

1) Humans determine <u>which plants</u> are grown in greenhouses and <u>fertilise</u> them. They also get rid of <u>pests</u> and <u>weeds</u>.

2) The <u>temperature</u>, <u>carbon dioxide level</u>, <u>light intensity</u> and <u>soil type</u> can all be controlled too, so that as much healthy product as possible is produced.

Under-soil heaters

Fish Farms **are** Artificial Ecosystems Used to **Rear** Fish

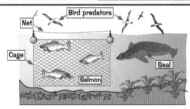

1) In fish farms, the conditions are managed to ensure the <u>best possible growth</u> of a single species of fish (e.g. trout, salmon).

2) The fish are kept in cages so that they're <u>protected from predators</u>.

3) They're fed a <u>carefully controlled diet</u>, and <u>pests</u> like fish lice are killed.

**Many** Ecosystems **are Still** Unexplored

1) Many of the world's natural ecosystems are <u>still unexplored</u>.

2) Areas of rainforest are <u>so dense</u> that they're difficult to penetrate, and deep oceans are rarely visited because special vehicles are needed to withstand the <u>high pressures</u> found there. There's <u>no light</u> at the bottom of a deep ocean either, so it's difficult to see what's there.

3) This means that there are likely to be a great many <u>animal and plant species</u> yet to be discovered.

So, you can still boldly go where no one has been before...

A lot of our <u>current medicines</u> originate from rainforest ingredients. And it's likely that some of the as-yet-undiscovered species out there contain <u>new drugs</u> which can cure life-threatening diseases. Which is another reason why it might not be a good idea to cut down all the trees on the planet.

Classification

It seems to be a basic human urge to want to classify things — that's the case in biology anyway...

Classification _is Organising_ Living Organisms _into Groups_

1) Nowadays we classify organisms into groups based on <u>genetic similarities</u>. For example, bats, whales and humans have a similar bone pattern in their forelimbs, and are all <u>genetically</u> related. The classification system reflects these <u>similarities</u>.

2) Living things are divided into <u>kingdoms</u> (e.g. the animal kingdom, the plant kingdom). Kingdoms are then <u>subdivided</u> into smaller and smaller groups. An example of one of these smaller groups is a <u>genus</u>.

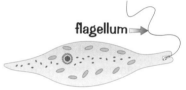

3) A <u>genus</u> is a group of closely-related <u>species</u> — and a species is a group of <u>closely-related</u> organisms that can breed to produce <u>fertile offspring</u> (see the next page).

Living Things _Can be_ Plants, Animals _or Something Else_

1) To be a member of the plant kingdom, organisms must contain <u>chloroplasts</u> and therefore be able to <u>make their own food</u> by photosynthesis (see page 25). Plants are fixed in the <u>ground</u> by their <u>roots</u>, so their movements are confined to <u>spreading out</u> to catch as much light and water as possible.

2) Members of the <u>animal</u> kingdom move about from place to place and they've got <u>compact</u> bodies — after all, you don't want to be sprawled out like a tree if you have to move about. Animals <u>can't make their own food</u>, so they have to find things to eat, such as plants.

3) Other living things, such as <u>fungi</u> and <u>bacteria</u>, don't have animal or plant characteristics. So they are classified into <u>other kingdoms</u>.

4) Some single-celled organisms have features of <u>both</u> plants and animals. <u>Euglena</u> can <u>move</u> from place to place by thrashing its <u>flagellum</u>, but also has <u>chloroplasts</u> which allow it to make its own food. It's put into a kingdom called <u>Protoctista</u>, along with some other single-celled organisms.

flagellum →

Euglena

Vertebrates _Have Backbones_

The animal kingdom is divided into <u>vertebrates</u> and <u>invertebrates</u>. Vertebrates are animals with a <u>backbone</u> and an <u>internal skeleton</u> — these help the animals move and protect their internal organs. Invertebrates don't have these structures — some of them do have an <u>external skeleton</u> though.

<u>Vertebrates</u> are divided into five groups, called <u>classes</u> — fish, amphibians, reptiles, birds and mammals.

1) <u>FISH</u> live in water. They have <u>scales</u> and slits (called <u>gills</u>) in the side of their heads for gas exchange.

2) <u>AMPHIBIANS</u> exchange gas partly through their skin, so gases have to be able to move in and out — their skin's got to be <u>permeable</u> and <u>moist</u>.

3) <u>REPTILES</u> are more adapted to live on the land. They've got a <u>dry scaly skin</u> which stops them losing too much water.

4) Most <u>BIRDS</u> can fly and they've got <u>feathers</u> to help them do this. You'll also find a <u>beak</u> — very useful for cracking seeds or catching prey.

5) <u>MAMMALS</u> have <u>fur</u> covering their bodies to keep them warm. They give birth to their young (not eggs like other vertebrates) and <u>produce milk</u> to feed them.

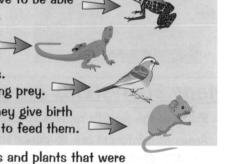

The rules of the classification system were made up using the animals and plants that were known about at the time. Sometimes <u>newly discovered species</u> don't really fit into any of the categories. These can be <u>living species</u> or <u>fossil ones</u>, such as <u>archaeopteryx</u>, which had reptilian teeth, clawed hands and a long bony tail, like a dinosaur, but also had wings and flight feathers, like a bird.

I'm not a vertebrate — I'm completely spineless...

There are <u>loads</u> of different types of organisms out there — so no wonder the classification system gets a bit unwieldy. This makes life no easier for you, I'm afraid — you've just got to <u>learn</u> it...

<u>*Species*</u>

There are millions of species. And you need to know them all for your exam. (Just kidding.)

The <u>Binomial System</u> Gives Everything a <u>Two-part Name</u>

In the <u>binomial system</u>, each species is given a <u>two-part</u> Latin name. The <u>first</u> part refers to the <u>genus</u> that the organism belongs to and the <u>second</u> part refers to the <u>species</u>.

> E.g. <u>Humans</u> are known as <u>Homo sapiens</u>. 'Homo' is the <u>genus</u> that they belong to and 'sapiens' is the <u>species</u>.

<u>Things of the</u> Same Species <u>Can Breed to Produce</u> Fertile Offspring

1) Organisms are of the <u>same species</u> if they can <u>breed</u> to produce <u>fertile offspring</u>.

2) If you interbreed a male from one species with a female from a <u>different</u> species you'll get a <u>hybrid</u> (that's if you get anything at all). For example, a <u>mule</u> is a cross between a donkey and a horse. But hybrids are <u>infertile</u> so they <u>aren't</u> new species — this makes it <u>difficult</u> to classify them.

<u>Unrelated Species</u> May Have Similar Features

1) Similar species often share a <u>recent common ancestor</u>, so they're <u>closely related</u> in evolutionary terms. They often look very <u>alike</u> and tend to live in similar types of <u>habitat</u>, e.g. whales and dolphins.

2) This isn't always the case though — closely related species may look <u>very different</u> if they have evolved to live in <u>different habitats</u>, e.g. llamas and camels.

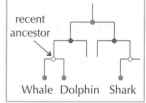

3) Species that are <u>very different genetically</u> may also end up looking alike. E.g. dolphins and sharks look pretty similar and swim in a similar way. But they're totally different species — dolphins are <u>mammals</u> and sharks are <u>fish</u>. They have evolved from <u>different ancestors</u> but they've <u>developed</u> similar bone structures which make them well adapted for <u>swimming</u>.

4) So to explain the similarities and differences between species, you have to consider how they're related in <u>evolutionary terms</u> AND the <u>type of environment</u> they've adapted to survive in.

<u>Keys</u> are Used to <u>Identify Creatures</u>

1) A <u>key</u> is a <u>series of questions</u> that you can use to figure out what an unknown organism is.

2) You start at question 1, the answer to the question (which you know by looking at your mystery organism) is used to <u>narrow down</u> your options of what it could be.

3) As you answer more and more questions you <u>narrow down your options further</u> until eventually you're just <u>left with one</u> possible species your organism could be.

Example: A student saw the following living things in a pond. Using the key provided, work out what each organism is.

1) Can the organism produce its own food?	..................YES, then it's a ..waterlily.. ....NO — go to question 2
2) Does the organism have a backbone?	..................YES — go to question 3 ....NO, then it's a ..dragonfly..
3) Does the organism have gills?	..................YES, then it's a ..fish... ....NO, then it's a ..frog...

Binomial system — uh oh, sounds like maths...

It's possible to breed lions and tigers together — it's true — they produce <u>hybrids</u> called tigons and ligers. They look a bit like lions and a bit like tigers... as you'd expect. In the same way, a bat is (probably) just a hybrid of a bird and a cat. And a donkey is the result of breeding a dog and a monkey.

Populations

Population size is how many of one particular type of plant or animal there is in an ecosystem
— there's lots about ecosystems on page 21.

Estimate Population Sizes Using a Quadrat

A quadrat is a square frame enclosing a known area. You just place it on the
ground, and look at what's inside it. To estimate population size:

1) Count all the organisms in a 1 m² quadrat.

2) Multiply the number of organisms by the total area (in m²) of the habitat.

3) Er, that's it. Bob's your uncle.

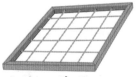

A quadrat

Example: Estimate the total populations of the various species in a 120 m² field if a 1 m² quadrat
contained 90 grass plants, 30 buttercups and 25 daisies.

Answer: Multiply the figures for the 1 m² quadrat by 120 to estimate the populations in the whole field.
So the field will contain about 10 800 grass plants, 3600 buttercups and 3000 daisies.

Estimating Population Sizes Using Mark-Release-Capture

All animals move about, so in order to count them, you'll have to catch them first.
Here's how:

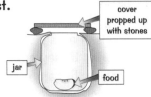

cover
propped up
with stones

jar

food

A pitfall trap

Nets — these are good for catching flying insects.

Pitfall traps — normally used to catch insects that walk across the ground.
The insects fall into the trap and are... well, trapped.

Pooters — these suck up individual insects chosen by the user.

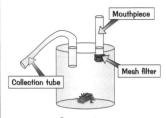

Mouthpiece

Mesh filter

Collection tube

A pooter

To estimate population size:

1) Capture a sample of the population and mark the animals in a harmless way.

2) Release them back into the environment.

3) Recapture another sample of the population. Count how many of this
sample are marked.

4) Estimate population size using this equation:

Population Size = $\dfrac{\text{no. animals in first sample} \times \text{no. animals in second sample}}{\text{no. of marked animals in second sample}}$

Example: A pitfall trap was set up in an area of woodland. 30 woodlice were caught in an hour and marked
on their shell with some non-toxic UV dye, before being released back into the environment.
The next day, 35 woodlice were caught in an hour, only 5 of which were marked. Estimate the
population size.

Answer: Multiply the number of woodlice in the first sample by the number in the second sample,
then divide the answer by the number that were marked in the second sample.
So the area of woodland will contain about (30 × 35) ÷ 5 = 210 woodlice.

Two Important Points About These Counting Methods:

1) The sample size affects the accuracy of the estimate — the bigger your sample, the more accurate
your estimate of the total population is likely to be.

2) The sample may not be representative of the population, i.e. what you find in your sample might be
different from what you'd have found if you'd looked somewhere else.

Counting methods — avoid the pit-falls...

This stuff sounds a right laugh — running around waving nets and setting traps for unsuspecting ants.
All in the name of science too. Remember — some animals prefer certain environments. E.g. there'll
be loads more woodlice hanging out underneath rocks than there are pootling about in an open field.

Photosynthesis

Plants can make their own food — it's ace. Here's how...

Photosynthesis Produces Glucose from Sunlight

1) <u>Photosynthesis</u> uses <u>energy</u> from the Sun to change <u>carbon dioxide</u> and <u>water</u> into <u>glucose</u> and <u>oxygen</u>.
2) It takes place in the <u>chloroplasts</u> of plant cells.
3) Chloroplasts contain <u>chlorophyll</u> that <u>absorbs</u> the <u>light</u> energy.

<u>Learn</u> these equations for photosynthesis:

$$\text{Carbon dioxide} + \text{Water} \xrightarrow[\text{chlorophyll}]{\text{LIGHT}} \text{glucose} + \text{oxygen}$$

$$6CO_2 + 6H_2O \longrightarrow C_6H_{12}O_6 + 6O_2$$

Glucose is Converted into Other Substances

<u>GLUCOSE</u> is <u>SOLUBLE</u>, which makes it really good for <u>transporting</u> to other places in the plant. It's also a <u>small</u> molecule — so it can <u>diffuse</u> in and out of cells <u>easily</u>.

Here's how plants use the glucose they make:

For Respiration ①

Plants use some of the <u>GLUCOSE</u> for <u>RESPIRATION</u>. This releases <u>energy</u> so they can <u>convert</u> the rest of the glucose into various other useful substances.

Stored in Seeds ③

<u>GLUCOSE</u> is turned into <u>LIPIDS</u> (fats and oils) for storing in <u>SEEDS</u>. <u>Sunflower seeds</u>, for example, contain a lot of oil — we get <u>cooking oil</u> and <u>margarine</u> from them.

Making Proteins ⑤

<u>GLUCOSE</u> is combined with <u>nitrates</u> (collected from the <u>soil</u>) to make <u>amino acids</u>, which are then made into <u>PROTEINS</u>. These are used for <u>growth</u> and <u>repair</u>.

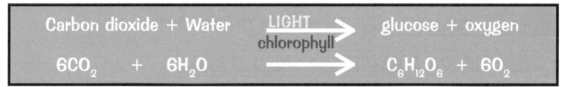

② *Making Cell walls*

<u>GLUCOSE</u> is converted into <u>CELLULOSE</u> for making <u>cell walls</u>, especially in a rapidly growing plant.

④ *Stored as Starch*

<u>GLUCOSE</u> is turned into <u>STARCH</u> and <u>stored</u> in roots, stems and leaves, ready for use when photosynthesis isn't happening, like at <u>night</u>.

<u>STARCH</u> is <u>INSOLUBLE</u>, which makes it much <u>better</u> for <u>storing</u> — it doesn't bloat the storage cells by <u>drawing water</u> in like glucose would.

Convert this page into stored information...

<u>Photosynthesis</u> is important. All the energy we get from eating comes from it. When we eat <u>plants</u>, we're consuming the energy they've made, and when we eat <u>meat</u>, we're eating animals who got their energy from eating plants, or from eating animals that have eaten other animals who have... and so on.

Rate of Photosynthesis

There are <u>three</u> factors that <u>control</u> the <u>rate</u> of photosynthesis — they're called <u>limiting factors</u>.

1) *Not Enough LIGHT Slows Down the Rate of Photosynthesis*

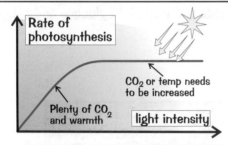

<u>Light</u> provides the <u>energy</u> needed for photosynthesis.

1) If the <u>light level</u> is raised, the rate of photosynthesis will <u>increase</u>, but only up to a <u>certain point</u>.

2) Beyond that, it won't make any <u>difference</u> because then it'll be either the <u>temperature</u> or the CO_2 level which is now the limiting factor.

2) *Too Little CARBON DIOXIDE Also Slows It Down*

CO_2 is one of the <u>raw materials</u> needed for photosynthesis — only <u>0.04%</u> of the air is CO_2, so it's <u>pretty scarce</u> as far as plants are concerned.

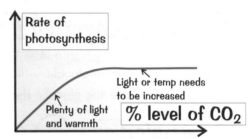

1) As with light intensity, the amount of CO_2 will only <u>increase</u> the rate of photosynthesis up to a point. After this the graph <u>flattens out</u>, showing that CO_2 is no longer the limiting factor.

2) As long as <u>light</u> and <u>CO_2</u> are in plentiful supply then the factor limiting photosynthesis must be <u>temperature</u>.

3) *The TEMPERATURE Has to be Just Right*

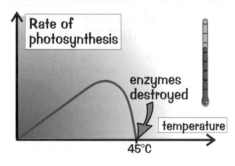

<u>Photosynthesis</u> works best when it's <u>warm but not too hot</u>.

1) As the <u>temperature increases</u>, so does the <u>rate</u> of photosynthesis. But if the <u>temperature</u> is too high, the plant's <u>enzymes</u> will be <u>destroyed</u>, so the rate rapidly <u>decreases</u>.

2) This happens at about <u>45 °C</u> (which is pretty hot for outdoors, though greenhouses can get that hot if you're not careful).

3) <u>Usually</u> though, if the temperature is the <u>limiting factor</u> it's because it's too low, and things need <u>warming up a bit</u>.

Photosynthesis and Respiration are OPPOSITE Processes

1) Plants use <u>photosynthesis</u> to trap <u>light</u> energy, and turn <u>carbon dioxide</u> and <u>water</u> into <u>oxygen</u> and <u>glucose</u>. <u>Respiration</u> uses <u>oxygen</u> and <u>glucose</u> and turns it back into <u>carbon dioxide</u> and <u>water</u>. These are opposite processes...

> <u>Photosynthesis</u>: carbon dioxide + water → glucose + oxygen   (<u>Requires</u> energy)

> <u>Respiration</u>: glucose + oxygen → carbon dioxide + water   (Energy <u>released</u>)

2) <u>Photosynthesis</u> only happens during the day. But plants <u>respire</u> all the time, day and night.

3) During the <u>day</u>, plants <u>make</u> more <u>oxygen</u> by photosynthesis than they use in respiration. So in daylight, they release oxygen and take in carbon dioxide.

4) At night though, plants only respire — there's no light for photosynthesis. This means they take in oxygen and release carbon dioxide — just like us.

Life isn't all fun and sunshine...

There are three limiting factors, a graph for each and an explanation of why it levels off or falls abruptly. You've then got to <u>learn</u> about respiration. Make sure you memorise those equations...

Interactions Between Organisms

Population Size is Limited by Available Resources

Population size is limited by:

1) The total amount of food or nutrients available (plants don't eat, but they get minerals from the soil).
2) The amount of water available.
3) The amount of light available (this applies only to plants really).
4) The quality and amount of shelter available.

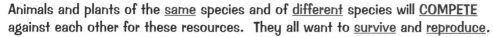

Animals and plants of the same species and of different species will COMPETE against each other for these resources. They all want to survive and reproduce.

Similar organisms will be in the closest competition — they'll be competing for the same ecological niche.

> **Example: Red and Grey Squirrels**
> 1) These two different species like the same kind of habitat, same kind of food, type of shelter, etc.
> 2) Grey squirrels are better adapted to deciduous woodland, so when they were introduced into Britain, red squirrels disappeared from many areas — they just couldn't compete.

So, a certain species will live in a particular area if it contains the resources it needs. But even if there's enough food and water in this area, another species may out-compete them for it — it's a hard life.

Populations of Prey and Predators Go in Cycles

In a community containing prey and predators (as most of them do of course):

1) The population of any species is usually limited by the amount of food available.
2) If the population of the prey increases, then so will the population of the predators.
3) However as the population of predators increases, the number of prey will decrease.

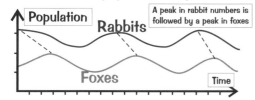

A peak in rabbit numbers is followed by a peak in foxes

e.g. More grass means more rabbits.
More rabbits means more foxes.
But more foxes means less rabbits.
Eventually less rabbits will mean less foxes again.
This up and down pattern continues...

Parasites and Mutualistic Relationships

The survival of some organisms can depend almost entirely on the presence of other species.

1) PARASITES live off a host. They take what they need to survive, without giving anything back. This often harms the host — which makes it a win-lose situation.

> • Tapeworms absorb lots of nutrients from the host, causing them to suffer from malnutrition.
> • Fleas are parasites. Dogs gain nothing from having fleas (unless you count hundreds of bites).

2) MUTUALISM is a relationship where both organisms benefit — so it's a win-win relationship.

> • Most plants have to rely on nitrogen-fixing bacteria in the soil to get the nitrates that they need. But leguminous plants carry the bacteria in nodules in their roots. The bacteria get a constant supply of sugar from the plant, and the plant gets essential nitrates from the bacteria.
> • 'Cleaner species' are fantastic. E.g. oxpeckers live on the backs of buffalo. Not only do they eat pests on the buffalo, like ticks, flies and maggots (providing the oxpeckers with a source of food), but they also alert the animal to any predators that are near, by hissing.

Revision stress — don't let it eat you up...

Ugh... I can't believe there are animals out there that actually eat ticks and maggots. Makes me feel ill just thinking about it. That said, I do like the idea of something watching my back — that's kinda cool.

Adaptation

The better an animal is adapted to its environment, the better it's able to compete for the resources...

The Polar Bear — Adapted for Cold Arctic Conditions

Polar bears have the following features, making them able to survive in chilly conditions:

1) <u>Large size</u> and <u>compact shape</u> (i.e. rounded), including dinky little ears, to keep the <u>surface area</u> to a minimum (compared to the body weight) — this all <u>reduces heat loss</u>.
2) A thick layer of <u>blubber</u> for <u>insulation</u> and also to survive hard times when food is scarce.
3) <u>Thick hairy coat</u> for keeping the body heat in.
4) <u>White fur</u> to match the surroundings for <u>camouflage</u>.
5) <u>Big feet</u> to <u>spread the weight</u> on snow and ice.
6) To help them <u>catch</u> their <u>prey</u>, they're <u>strong swimmers</u> and <u>runners</u>. They've also got <u>sharp claws</u> and <u>teeth</u>.
7) <u>Fur on soles of paws</u> to help <u>grip</u> the snow and ice, and to <u>keep heat in</u>.

The Camel — Adapted for Dry Desert Conditions

1) Camels can <u>store</u> a lot of <u>water</u> without a problem.
2) They store <u>fat</u> in their <u>hump</u> — they use the fat for energy on long journeys where there's no food. This means the rest of the body <u>isn't insulated</u>, helping heat loss.
3) They can tolerate <u>big changes</u> in their own <u>body temperature</u>, from 34 °C to 41 °C.
4) They have a <u>thick coat</u> that <u>reflects sunlight</u> in the day (keeping them <u>cool</u>) and keeps them <u>warm</u> at <u>night</u> when it's cold (yes, it does get cold in the desert).
5) <u>Bushy eyelashes</u> and <u>hair-lined nostrils</u> that can close to <u>stop sand</u> getting in.
6) <u>Large feet</u> to <u>spread load</u> on soft sand.

The Cactus is Well Adapted for Hot Dry Conditions

1) Cacti have a <u>small surface area</u> compared to their volume to <u>reduce water loss</u>.
2) They've got a <u>thick waxy layer</u> (called a <u>cuticle</u>) and <u>leaves reduced to spines</u> to further <u>reduce water loss</u>.
3) They <u>store water</u> in their thick stem. In times when there's not much water around they can use this water to survive.
4) Instead of leaves, the <u>green</u> stem carries out <u>photosynthesis</u>.
5) It has <u>sharp spines</u>, to stop herbivores eating it.
6) It has <u>shallow</u>, but very extensive roots, to ensure water is <u>absorbed</u> quickly over a large area.

Plants Use Either Wind or Insects for Pollination

Plants reproduce by transferring <u>pollen</u> to the <u>stigmas</u> of other plants of the same species. Most use the <u>wind</u> or <u>insects</u> to carry the pollen, and they've <u>adapted</u> to whichever method they use.

1) WIND POLLINATION

These plants have <u>long</u>, <u>feathery stigmas</u> to provide a <u>large surface area</u> to trap pollen.
Their <u>pollen</u> grains are <u>light</u> and <u>dry</u>, which helps the wind <u>carry</u> them to the stigmas.

2) INSECT POLLINATION

These plants have <u>brightly coloured scented petals</u> and <u>scented nectar</u> to attract insects.
Their <u>pollen</u> grains are <u>large</u> and <u>sticky</u>, so that when an insect lands on the flower the pollen grains get stuck to them. They then carry them to the next plant.

That's a lovely cravat — no it's not, it's a cacti...

<u>Moral of the story</u>, adapt or become out-competed and die. Harsh, but true. You've got to change to survive, and the better you are at it, the better you'll do in life. No one's saying it's easy though...

Fossils

Fossils are the Remains of Plants and Animals

Fossils are evidence of organisms that lived ages ago. There are three ways fossils can be formed:

1) FROM GRADUAL REPLACEMENT BY MINERALS (Most fossils happen this way.)

Things like teeth, shells, bones etc., which don't decay easily, can last a long time when buried. They're eventually replaced by minerals as they decay, forming a rock-like substance shaped like the original hard part. The surrounding sediments also turn to rock, but the fossil stays distinct inside the rock and eventually someone digs it up.

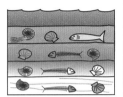

2) FROM CASTS AND IMPRESSIONS

Sometimes, fossils are formed when an organism is buried in a soft material like clay. The clay later hardens around it and the organism decays, leaving a cast of itself. Things like footprints can be pressed into these materials when soft, leaving an impression when it hardens.

3) FROM PRESERVATION IN PLACES WHERE NO DECAY HAPPENS

a) In amber (a clear yellow 'stone' made from fossilised resin) and tar pits there's no oxygen or moisture so decay microbes can't survive.

b) In glaciers it's too cold for the decay microbes to work.

c) Peat bogs are too acidic for decay microbes. (A fully preserved man they named 'Pete Marsh' was found in a bog.)

The Fossil Record is Incomplete

Suggested evolution of the horse

Body   Forefeet

1) Fossils provide lots of evidence for the theory of evolution.

> The theory of evolution suggests that all the animals and plants on Earth gradually "evolved" over millions of years, rather than just simply popping into existence.

2) Fossils show how many of today's species have changed and developed over millions of years. But there are quite a few "missing links" because the fossil record is incomplete.

3) This is because very very few dead plants or animals actually turn into fossils, and some body parts, like soft tissue, tend to decay away completely.

4) There are fossils yet to be discovered that might help complete the picture.

The Evolution of the Horse

1) The fossil record of the horse provides strong evidence for the theory of evolution, but things are a little more complicated than we first thought.

2) If you stick all the fossil bones in order of age, they seem to show the modern horse evolving gradually from a creature about the size of a dog, with the middle toe slowly getting bigger and bigger to form the familiar hoof of today's horse.

3) The trouble is, some of the fossils didn't seem to fit so well. But nowadays we know that several now-extinct kinds of horse evolved at the same time, and it all makes perfect sense. Hurrah.

There are Other Views About the Fossil Record

1) Some people don't believe in evolution, and they interpret the fossil evidence differently.

2) This is sometimes part of a religious belief. For example, creationists believe that each species was created separately by God and will never evolve into a new species. They believe the fossil record is not evidence for gradual evolution, but simply shows a lot of different organisms, some of which are now extinct.

Don't get bogged down by all this information...

The fossil record provides good evidence for evolution, but it can't prove it. But proving a theory of something that happens over millions of years was never going to be straightforward, I guess.

Theories of Evolution

It's the genetic variation between the individuals of a species that makes evolution possible.

Only the Fittest Survive

1) Charles Darwin <u>knew</u> that organisms in a species showed <u>wide variation</u>, and that parents <u>passed on</u> characteristics to their children. He also knew organisms have to <u>compete</u> for resources, and may be eaten or catch disease.

2) Darwin concluded that all organisms must have to <u>struggle for survival</u>.

3) The ones who have the most <u>successful adaptations</u> are the ones who are most likely to <u>survive, reproduce and pass on their genes</u>. This is the theory of <u>natural selection</u>.

4) As environments <u>change</u>, certain <u>adaptations</u> will be better <u>suited</u>. If a variation gives organisms a survival advantage it is likely to become <u>more common</u> in the population.

5) Over a long period of time, these evolved adaptations may even lead to a <u>new species</u>.

6) If a species can't evolve <u>quick enough</u> it may become <u>extinct</u>.

Darwin's theory stirred up a fair bit of trouble in its time. For the first time ever, there was a highly plausible explanation for our own existence, without the need for a "<u>Creator</u>". This was very bad news for the <u>religious authorities</u> of the time, who ridiculed his ideas.

Modern Examples of Natural Selection

1) Peppered Moths Adapted Their Colour

<u>Peppered moths</u> are often seen on the <u>bark</u> of trees. Until the 19th century, the only ones found in England were <u>light</u> in colour. Then some areas became <u>polluted</u> and the soot darkened the tree trunks. A <u>black</u> variety of moth was found. The moths had <u>adapted</u> to stay <u>camouflaged</u>.

2) Bacteria Adapt to Beat Antibiotics

The "<u>survival of the fittest</u>" affects bacteria just the same as other living things. They adapt to become <u>resistant</u> to our bacterial weapons — <u>antibiotics</u>.

1) If someone gets ill they might be given an <u>antibiotic</u> which <u>kills</u> 99% of the bacteria.

2) The 1% that survive are <u>resistant</u> so if they're passed on to somebody else, the antibiotic won't help them.

Nowadays bacteria are getting resistant at such a rate the development of antibiotics <u>can't keep up</u>. Eeek!

3) Rats Adapt to Beat Poison

The poison <u>warfarin</u> was widely used to control the <u>rat</u> population. However, a certain gene gives rats <u>resistance</u> to it, so rats which carry it are more likely to survive and breed. This gene has become more and more <u>frequent</u> in the rat population, so warfarin isn't as much use any more.

Lamarck Had a Conflicting Theory of Evolution

Darwin's <u>theory of evolution</u> wasn't the only one. Lamarck had a different idea:

1) <u>Lamarck</u> argued that if a <u>characteristic</u> was <u>used a lot</u> by an animal then it would become more <u>developed</u>. Lamarck reckoned that these <u>acquired characteristics</u> could be passed on to the <u>animal's offspring</u>. For example, if a rabbit did a lot of running and developed big leg muscles, Lamarck believed that the rabbit's offspring would also have big leg muscles.

2) But people eventually concluded that acquired characteristics <u>don't</u> have a <u>genetic basis</u> — so they're <u>unable</u> to be passed on to the next generation. This is why Lamarck's theory was rejected.

"Natural selection" — sounds like vegan chocolates...

Natural selection's all about the organisms with the <u>best characteristics</u> surviving to <u>pass on their genes</u> so that the whole species ends up <u>adapted</u> to its environment. It doesn't happen overnight though.

Human Impact on the Environment

Pollution is one of the hot topics in the news at the moment (literally, if you're talking global warming).

Human Population is Increasing

1) The world's human population is rising <u>exponentially</u> — which means it's <u>increasing very quickly</u>.

2) This rapidly increasing population is putting loads of pressure on the <u>environment</u> — more resources are being used up and more pollution's being produced.

3) The <u>higher standard</u> of living amongst more <u>developed</u> countries demands even more resources, and although these developed countries have only a <u>small proportion</u> of the world's population, they cause a <u>large proportion</u> of the pollution.

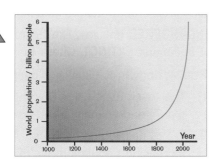

Increasing Amounts of Pollution are Causing...

1) Global Warming and Acid Rain

1) <u>Fossil fuels</u> are <u>coal</u>, <u>oil</u> and <u>natural gas</u>.

2) When they're burned, they release lots of <u>carbon dioxide</u>, which causes <u>global warming</u>, and <u>sulfur dioxide</u>, which causes <u>acid rain</u>.

3) Fossil fuels are mainly burned in <u>cars</u> and <u>power stations</u>.

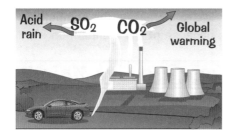

Acid rain ← SO_2 CO_2 → Global warming

2) Ozone Depletion

1) <u>CFCs</u> (chlorofluorocarbons) used to be used in <u>aerosols</u>, <u>fridges</u>, <u>air-conditioning units</u>, and <u>polystyrene foam</u>.

2) They break down <u>ozone</u> in the upper atmosphere.

3) This allows more <u>harmful UV rays</u> to reach the Earth's surface.

4) Being exposed to more UV rays will increase the risk of <u>skin cancer</u> (although this can be reduced with suncream). Australia has high levels of skin cancer because it is under an ozone hole.

5) The increase in UV rays might also <u>kill plankton</u> in the sea — this could have a massive effect on the <u>sea ecosystem</u> because plankton are at the bottom of the food chain. Scientists predict that <u>fish levels</u> will <u>drop</u> (meaning, among other things, <u>less food</u> for us to eat).

Indicator Species Show Pollution Levels

By looking for <u>indicator species</u>, you can tell if an area is <u>polluted</u> or not.

1) Some species can only survive in <u>unpolluted conditions</u>, so if you find lots of them, you know it's a <u>clean area</u>.

> <u>Lichens</u> are used to monitor <u>air quality</u> — they're damaged by pollution. The <u>cleaner</u> the air, the <u>greater</u> the <u>diversity</u> of lichens that survive.

2) Other species have adapted to live in <u>polluted conditions</u> — so if you see a lot of them you know there's a problem.

> <u>Bloodworms</u>, <u>water lice</u>, <u>rat-tailed maggots</u> and <u>sludgeworms</u> all indicate <u>polluted</u> water. But out of these, <u>rat-tailed maggots</u> and <u>sludgeworms</u> indicate a <u>very high level of pollution</u>.

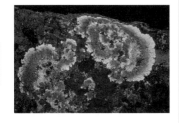

Sludgeworms and rat-tailed maggots — harbingers of doom...

More people means <u>more demand</u> for food, energy, land and raw materials — and more waste and pollution. The worst culprits are people like us in <u>developed countries</u> who want energy for their air-conditioners and 'need' their food triple-wrapped. Still, I guess the <u>sludgeworms</u> aren't complaining...

Endangered Species

Loads of species are endangered these days. And in many cases, it's all our fault.

We're Endangering Many Species

Kill, kill, kill, oops they're all dead. Chop, chop, chop, oops they're homeless... and dead.
ENDANGERED species, like tigers, have very low numbers left in the wild. They're in danger of becoming EXTINCT, where there's none of them at all — like the dodo and woolly mammoth.

Human activity is causing a decrease in the population sizes of many species.

1) The fossil fuels we're burning are thought to be causing the climate to change — plants and animals aren't able to adapt fast enough to cope with these changes.

2) We're destroying habitats. As we chop down trees, making room for our rapidly increasing population, we're demolishing the homes of thousands of different species.

3) Many animals are hunted — some for food, others for fur coats or jewellery, and some just for fun.

4) Humans cause pollution which harms many living things. E.g. pesticides and other pollutants in rivers contributed to otters becoming endangered.

5) We're increasing the competition between species. For example, red squirrels are now endangered because of the competition from grey squirrels — which we introduced to Britain. See page 27.

There are Five Main Ways to Protect Endangered Species

There's stuff we can do to help save endangered plants and animals:

1) EDUCATION PROGRAMMES — organisations like the RSPB and Greenpeace teach people what to do (and often what not to do) to protect endangered species.

2) PROTECTED HABITATS — organisations like the National Trust obtain and preserve sites such as woodlands. Sometimes habitats are protected with a particular species in mind. E.g. red squirrel refuges — these are surrounded by buffer zones that grey squirrels are unlikely to cross and game keepers are employed to get rid of any that do get in.

3) LEGAL PROTECTION — legislation is sometimes used to stop people from doing even more damage. For example, it's illegal to hunt protected species, or to damage their homes.

4) CAPTIVE BREEDING — breeding from endangered species in captivity (e.g. in zoos) can increase their numbers. Animals born in captivity can sometimes be re-introduced to the wild.

5) CREATING ARTIFICIAL ECOSYSTEMS — sometimes an artificial ecosystem can be created in which the conditions are controlled to favour the endangered species (e.g. botanical gardens).

Conservation Programmes Benefit Wildlife and Humans

Conservation programmes do more than just benefit endangered species — they often help humans too:

1) PROTECTING THE HUMAN FOOD SUPPLY — over-fishing has greatly reduced fish stocks in the world's oceans, and conservation programmes can ensure that future generations can have fish to eat.

2) REDUCING THE NEED FOR CHEMICAL PESTICIDES — protecting predators of pests, such as ladybirds which eat aphids, means crops can be grown without using potentially harmful chemical pesticides.

3) PROVIDING FUTURE MEDICINES — many of the medicines we use today come from plants. Undiscovered plant species may contain new medicinal chemicals. If these plants are allowed to become extinct, perhaps through rainforest destruction, we could miss out on valuable medicines.

4) CULTURAL ASPECTS — individual species may be important in a nation's or an area's cultural heritage, e.g. the bald eagle is being conserved in the USA as it is regarded as a national symbol.

Neighbours from hell — that's us, that is...

We really don't make good neighbours for wildlife. But even if you're someone who hates all plants and animals and much prefers concrete, remember that there are human benefits to protecting wildlife.

Sustainable Development

It's not all doom and gloom... if we do things sustainably we'll be OK.

Development Has to be Sustainable

As the human population gets bigger...

1) We need to <u>produce more food</u> — so we'll need more land for <u>farming</u>.

2) We use up <u>more energy</u>. At the moment the vast majority of energy comes from burning <u>fossil fuels</u>. But these are <u>rapidly running out</u> — we need to find an <u>alternative</u> energy source.

3) We're <u>producing more waste</u> — it all needs to be put somewhere and a lot of it's <u>polluting</u> the Earth.

We need to find a way to <u>exist</u> where we don't <u>damage</u> the environment.
A fancy term for this is '<u>sustainable development</u>':

> <u>SUSTAINABLE DEVELOPMENT</u> meets the needs of <u>today's</u> population <u>without</u> harming the ability of <u>future</u> generations to meet their own needs.

Sustainable development needs to be <u>carefully planned</u> and it needs to be carried out all over the Earth. This means there needs to be <u>cooperation locally</u>, <u>nationally</u> and <u>internationally</u>.

EXAMPLES OF WHAT'S BEING DONE TO PROMOTE SUSTAINABLE DEVELOPMENT:

1) <u>Fishing quotas</u> have been introduced to prevent some types of fish, such as cod, from becoming <u>extinct</u> in certain areas. This means they'll <u>still be around</u> in years to come.

2) To make the production of <u>wood</u> and <u>paper</u> sustainable there are laws insisting that logging companies <u>plant new trees</u> to replace those that they've felled.

<u>Education</u> is important. If people are <u>aware</u> of the problems, they may be more likely to <u>help</u> — e.g. by not buying certain types of fish and only buying wood products from sustainably managed forests. Sustainable development also helps <u>endangered species</u> by considering the impacts on their <u>habitats</u>.

Case Study: Whales — Some Species are Endangered

1) Whales have <u>commercial value</u> (they can be used to make money) when they're <u>alive</u> and <u>dead</u>.

2) They're a <u>tourist attraction</u> — people go to some areas especially to see the whales.

3) Whale <u>meat</u> and <u>oil</u> can be used, and <u>cosmetics</u> can be made from a waxy substance in their intestines. However, this has led to some species of whale becoming <u>endangered</u>.

4) The <u>International Whaling Commission</u> has struggled to get nations to agree to <u>restrict whaling</u>. In 1982 the member nations declared a <u>stop to whaling</u>, the only exception being Norway, which still catches whales. Taking a <u>small</u> number of whales ('culling') for <u>scientific research</u> is allowed and is carried out by Japan, Iceland and the Faroe Isles.

5) But it's hard to check that countries are sticking to the agreement, and a lot of <u>illegal whaling</u> goes on. <u>Whale meat</u> is regarded as a delicacy in some areas and it sells for very <u>high prices</u>.

6) Some whales are kept in <u>captivity</u> — there are <u>different views</u> about this:
   • Whales don't have much <u>space</u> in captivity and they are sometimes used for <u>entertaining</u> people. Some people think this is <u>wrong</u> and that the whales would be <u>much happier</u> in the wild, but captive whales do <u>increase awareness</u> of the animals and their problems.
   • <u>Captive breeding programmes</u> allow whales to be bred in numbers and <u>released</u> back into the wild.
   • <u>Research</u> on captive whales can help us <u>understand their needs</u> better to help <u>conservation</u>.

Fishermen are just too effishent... ^(groan...)

Whales are amazing animals — it'd be a huge pity if they were wiped out and weren't around for future generations. It's not just deliberate hunting that's a problem for them — they often get <u>tangled up</u> in fishing nets or <u>collide with ships</u>. And <u>pollution</u> doesn't do them much good either. It's a tough life.

Revision Summary for Module B2

Now it's time to find out if you know your stuff. This section covers everything from counting animals to sustainable development. You've got to know why a species lives where it does and what adaptations it has to help it along the way. Oh, and there's a little bit of photosynthesis splashed in for fun. If the answers to these questions don't roll off your tongue immediately, you've got to go back to the page and relearn the stuff. Here goes...

1) What's the difference between a natural and an artificial ecosystem? Give an example of each.
2) Name two different kingdoms.
3) What do all vertebrates have in common?
4) Name the five different types of vertebrate.
5) Why are euglena and archaeopteryx difficult to classify?
6) In the binomial system each organism is given a two-part name. What does each part refer to?
7) What is a species?
8) What do you get if you manage to breed two different species together?
9) Why might two unrelated species look very similar?
10) Why might two closely related species look very different?
11)* Devise a key to tell apart a worm, a snail, a centipede and a spider.
12) Describe how you use a quadrat to estimate population size.
13)*You catch 23 woodlice with a pooter one day and mark their shells. The next day you catch 28 woodlice and find that four of them are marked. Estimate the population size.
14) Where in a plant cell does photosynthesis take place?
15) Write down the word and symbol equations for photosynthesis.
16) Why is glucose easily transported around a plant? Why is starch good for storage of glucose?
17) Give three uses of glucose in plants.
18) What are the three limiting factors in photosynthesis?
19) When do plants respire?
20) Name four things that animals will compete against each other for.
21) Sketch a graph of prey and predator populations and explain the pattern shown.
22) What is the difference between a parasitic and a mutualistic relationship? Give an example of each.
23) Name five features of the following organisms that adapt them to their habitat:
a) polar bear, b) camel, c) cactus.
24) What are the two methods plants use for pollination? What features adapt them for each method?
25) Describe the three ways that fossils can form. Give an example of each type.
26) Explain how fossils found in rocks support the theory of evolution.
27) Describe three examples of natural selection.
28) How did Lamarck's theory contrast with Darwin's?
29) What problems does a rapidly increasing population create for a country?
30) Name a gas that causes acid rain. Where does this gas come from?
31) What are indicator species? Give examples.
32) Name five ways in which we're increasing the number of endangered species.
33) Name five ways in which we're trying to protect endangered species.
34) Why do environmentalists say we should be trying to implement conservation programmes?
35) What is sustainable development?
36) What are the commercial values of whales?
37) What are the pros and cons of keeping whales in captivity?

* Answers on page 108

Cells and DNA

Biology's all about living stuff. And all living stuff contains cells. So let's make a start with cells...

Plant and Animal Cells Have Similarities and Differences

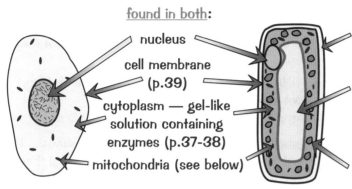

found in both:

- nucleus
- cell membrane (p.39)
- cytoplasm — gel-like solution containing enzymes (p.37-38)
- mitochondria (see below)

just found in plant cells:

- rigid cell wall made of cellulose — supports the cell
- large vacuole — contains cell sap (a weak solution of sugars and salts) and helps provide support
- chloroplasts (see p.59)

Energy for life processes is provided by respiration.

1) Most of the reactions involved in respiration take place in the mitochondria.
2) Respiration turns glucose and oxygen into water and carbon dioxide, and in doing so releases energy.

The Nucleus Contains DNA

1) DNA is found in the nucleus of every cell.
2) It is a double-stranded helix (double spiral). Each of the two strands is made up of lots of small groups called "nucleotides".
3) Each nucleotide contains a small molecule called a "base". DNA has just four different bases.
4) You only need to know the four bases by their first initials — A, C, G and T.
5) Each base forms cross links to a base on the other strand. This keeps the two DNA strands tightly wound together.
6) A always pairs up with T, and C always pairs up with G. This is called complementary base-pairing.

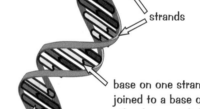

strands

base on one strand is joined to a base on the other by cross links

bases

DNA Can Replicate Itself

1) DNA copies itself every time a cell divides, so that each new cell still has the full amount of DNA.
2) In order to copy itself, the DNA double helix first 'unzips' — to form two single strands.
3) As the DNA unwinds itself, new nucleotides (floating about freely in the nucleus) join on only where the bases fit (A with T and C with G), making an exact copy of the DNA on the other strand.
4) The result is two molecules of DNA identical to the original molecule of DNA.

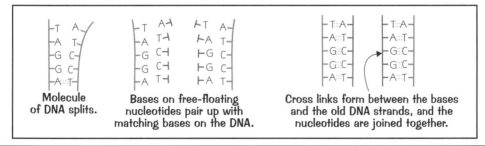

Molecule of DNA splits.

Bases on free-floating nucleotides pair up with matching bases on the DNA.

Cross links form between the bases and the old DNA strands, and the nucleotides are joined together.

Q: What do DNA and a game of rounders have in common...?

Answer: four bases, and don't you forget it. Scientists spent years and years trying to work out the structure of DNA, and in 1953 two of them finally cracked it. They were Francis Crick (British) and James Watson (American) and their discovery of the double helix led to them winning a Nobel Prize in 1962.

DNA Fingerprinting

Now this is more interesting — <u>forensic science</u> being used to catch murderers, just like on the telly.

Genetic Fingerprinting Pinpoints Individuals

1) Your DNA is <u>unique</u> (unless you're an identical twin — then the two of you have identical DNA).

2) <u>DNA fingerprinting</u> (or genetic fingerprinting) is a way of <u>comparing DNA samples</u> to see if they come from the same person or from two different people.

3) DNA fingerprinting is used in <u>forensic science</u>. DNA (from hair, skin flakes, blood, semen etc.) taken from a <u>crime scene</u> is compared with a DNA sample taken from a <u>suspect</u>.

4) It can also be used in <u>paternity tests</u> — to check if a man is the father of a particular child.

5) Some people would like there to be a national <u>genetic database</u> of everyone in the country. That way, DNA from a crime scene could be checked against <u>everyone</u> in the country to see whose it was. But others think this is a big <u>invasion of privacy</u>, and they worry about how <u>safe</u> the data would be and what <u>else</u> it might be used for. There are also <u>scientific problems</u> — <u>false positives</u> can occur if <u>errors</u> are made in the procedure or if the data is <u>misinterpreted</u>.

HOW IT WORKS

1) First you have to <u>isolate</u> the DNA from the cells.

2) Special <u>enzymes</u> are then used to <u>cut the DNA</u> into <u>fragments</u>. They cut it at every place where they recognise a <u>particular order of bases</u>. Where these sections are in the DNA will be <u>different for everyone</u>.

3) If the DNA sample contains that little section of bases <u>lots</u> of times, it'll be cut into lots of <u>little bits</u>. If it only contains it a <u>few</u> times, it'll be left in <u>bigger bits</u>.

4) The DNA bits are separated out using a process a bit like <u>chromatography</u>. They're <u>suspended in a gel</u>, and an <u>electric current</u> is passed through the gel. DNA is <u>negatively charged</u>, so it moves towards the <u>positive anode</u>. Small bits travel <u>faster</u> than big bits, so they get <u>further</u> through the gel.

5) The DNA is "tagged" with a <u>radioactive marker</u>. Then it's placed onto <u>photographic film</u>. The film goes <u>dark</u> where the radioactivity is, revealing the <u>positions</u> of the DNA fragments.

DNA moves towards the anode, with smallest fragments moving furthest

−ve cathode

DNA fragment (invisible)

gel

+ve anode

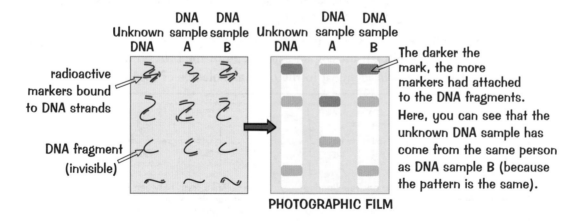

radioactive markers bound to DNA strands

DNA fragment (invisible)

Unknown DNA — DNA sample A — DNA sample B

Unknown DNA — DNA sample A — DNA sample B

PHOTOGRAPHIC FILM

The darker the mark, the more markers had attached to the DNA fragments.

Here, you can see that the unknown DNA sample has come from the same person as DNA sample B (because the pattern is the same).

So the trick is — frame your twin and they'll never get you...

In the exam you might have to interpret data on <u>DNA fingerprinting for identification</u>. They'd probably give you a diagram similar to the one at the bottom of this page, and you'd have to say <u>which</u> of the <u>known</u> samples (if any) <u>matched</u> the <u>unknown</u> sample. Pretty easy — it's the two that look the same.

Protein Synthesis and Enzymes

So here's how life works — DNA molecules contain a genetic code which determines which proteins are built. The proteins include enzymes that control all the reactions going on in the body. Simple, eh.

Proteins are Made by Reading the Code in DNA

1) DNA controls the production of proteins (protein synthesis) in a cell.

2) A gene is a section of DNA that 'codes' for a particular protein.

3) Proteins are made up of chains of molecules called amino acids. Each different protein has its own particular number and order of amino acids.

4) This gives each protein a different shape, which means each protein can have a different function.

5) It's the order of the bases in a strand of DNA that decides the order of amino acids in a protein.

6) Each amino acid is coded for by a sequence of three bases in the strand of DNA.

7) Proteins are made from 20 different amino acids, all found in the cytoplasm of cells. They're stuck together to make proteins, following the order of the code on the DNA.

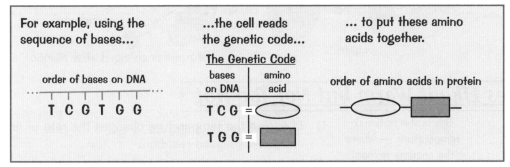

For example, using the sequence of bases...

order of bases on DNA

T C G T G G

...the cell reads the genetic code...

The Genetic Code

bases on DNA	amino acid
T C G =	
T G G =	

... to put these amino acids together.

order of amino acids in protein

8) We get amino acids from our diet. If we don't take in all the amino acids in the right amounts, our body can change some of them into others. This is called transamination and it happens in the liver.

Enzymes are Catalysts Produced by Living Things

1) Living things have thousands of different chemical reactions going on inside them all the time — like respiration, photosynthesis and protein synthesis.

2) These reactions need to be carefully controlled — to get the right amounts of substances and keep the organism working properly.

3) You can usually make a reaction happen more quickly by raising the temperature. This would speed up the useful reactions but also the unwanted ones too... not good. There's also a limit to how far you can raise the temperature inside a living creature before its cells start getting damaged.

4) So... living things produce enzymes which act as biological catalysts. Enzymes reduce the need for high temperatures and we only have enzymes to speed up the useful chemical reactions in the body.

> An ENZYME is a BIOLOGICAL CATALYST
> which INCREASES the speed of a reaction.

5) Enzymes are all proteins, which is one reason why proteins are so important to living things.

6) Every different biological reaction has its own enzyme designed especially for it.

7) Each enzyme is coded for by a different gene, and has a unique shape which it needs to do its job (see next page).

No horses were harmed in the making of this page...

...it's just our high-tech special effects that give that impression. Enzymes allow us to have a huge amount of control over which chemical reactions go on in our bodies. They're also useful outside the body — where we use them in things like biological washing powders.

Enzymes

The enzymes in our body are specific because they have a special <u>shape</u>.

Enzymes **are Very Specific**

1) <u>Chemical reactions</u> usually involve things either being <u>split apart</u> or <u>joined together</u>.

2) The <u>substrate</u> is the molecule <u>changed</u> in the reaction.

3) <u>Every</u> enzyme has an <u>active site</u> — the part where it <u>joins on</u> to its substrate to catalyse the reaction.

4) Enzymes are really <u>picky</u> — they usually only work with <u>one substrate</u>. The posh way of saying this is that enzymes have a <u>high specificity for their substrate</u>.

5) This is because, for the enzyme to work, the substrate has to <u>fit</u> into the <u>active site</u>. If the substrate's shape doesn't <u>match</u> the active site's shape, then the reaction <u>won't</u> be catalysed. This is called the <u>'lock and key' mechanism</u>, because the substrate fits into the enzyme just like a key fits into a lock.

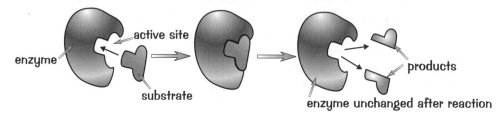

Enzymes **Like it Warm but Not Too Hot**

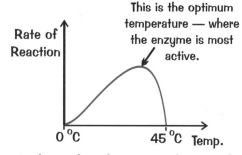

This is the optimum temperature — where the enzyme is most active.

1) Changing the <u>temperature</u> changes the <u>rate</u> of an enzyme-catalysed reaction.

2) Like with any reaction, a higher temperature <u>increases</u> the rate at first. This is because more <u>heat</u> means the enzymes and the substrate particles have more <u>energy</u>. They <u>move about</u> more, so they're more likely to meet up and react.

3) If it gets <u>too hot</u> though, some of the <u>bonds</u> holding the enzyme together <u>break</u>.

4) This makes the enzyme <u>lose its shape</u>. Its <u>active site</u> doesn't fit the shape of the substrate any more, so it <u>can't</u> catalyse the reaction and the reaction <u>stops</u>.

5) The enzyme is now said to be <u>denatured</u>. The shape change is <u>permanent</u> — it won't go back to normal if things <u>cool down</u> again.

6) Each enzyme has its own <u>optimum temperature</u> when the reaction goes <u>fastest</u>. This is the temperature just before it gets too hot and starts to denature. The optimum temperature for the most important <u>human</u> enzymes is about <u>37 °C</u> — the <u>same</u> temperature as our bodies. Lucky for us.

Enzymes **Like it the Right pH Too**

1) The <u>pH</u> also has an effect on enzymes.

2) If the pH is too high or too low, it interferes with the <u>bonds</u> holding the enzyme together. This changes the shape of the <u>active site</u> and <u>denatures</u> the enzyme.

3) All enzymes have an <u>optimum pH</u> that they work best at. It's often <u>neutral pH 7</u>, but <u>not always</u>. For example, <u>pepsin</u> is an enzyme used to break down <u>proteins</u> in the <u>stomach</u>. It works best at <u>pH 2</u>, which means it's well-suited to the <u>acidic conditions</u> in the stomach.

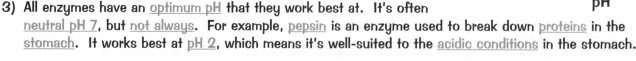

If the lock & key mechanism fails, you get in through a window...

Changing the <u>shape</u> of a protein totally changes it. <u>Egg white</u> contains lots of protein — think what happens when you boil an egg and <u>denature</u> the protein. It goes from clear and runny to white and solid.

Diffusion

Particles move about randomly, and after a bit they end up evenly spaced. And that's how most things move about in our bodies — by "diffusion"...

Don't be Put Off by the Fancy Word

"Diffusion" is simple. It's just the gradual movement of particles from places where there are lots of them to places where there are fewer of them. That's all it is — just the natural tendency for stuff to spread out. Unfortunately you also have to learn the fancy way of saying the same thing, which is this:

> **DIFFUSION is the PASSIVE MOVEMENT OF PARTICLES from an area of HIGHER CONCENTRATION to an area of LOWER CONCENTRATION**

Diffusion happens in both liquids and gases — that's because the particles in these substances are free to move about randomly. The simplest type is when different gases diffuse through each other. This is what's happening when the smell of perfume diffuses through a room:

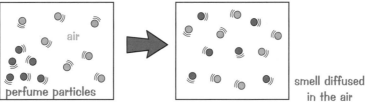

air

perfume particles

smell diffused in the air

Cell Membranes are Kind of Clever...

They're clever because they hold the cell together BUT they let stuff in and out as well. Only very small molecules can diffuse through cell membranes though — things like simple sugars, water or ions. Big molecules like starch and proteins can't pass through the membrane.

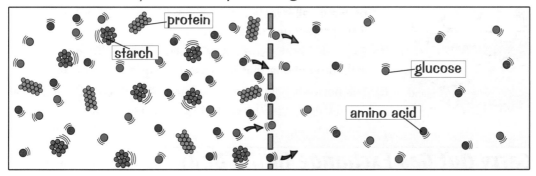

protein

starch

glucose

amino acid

1) Just like with diffusion in air, particles flow through the cell membrane from where there's a higher concentration (a lot of them) to where there's a lower concentration (not such a lot of them).

2) They're only moving about randomly of course, so they go both ways — but if there are a lot more particles on one side of the membrane, there's obviously an overall movement from that side.

3) The rate of diffusion depends on three main things:

   a) Distance — substances diffuse more quickly when they haven't as far to move. Pretty obvious.

   b) Concentration difference (gradient) — substances diffuse faster if there's a big difference in concentration. If there are lots more particles on one side, there are more there to move across.

   c) Surface area — the more surface there is available for molecules to move across, the faster they can get from one side to the other.

Whoever smelt it dealt it... Whoever said the rhyme did the crime...

Because, of course, it's not just perfume that diffuses through a room. Anyway. All living cells have membranes, and their structure allows sugars, water and the rest to drift in and out as needed. Don't forget, the membrane doesn't control diffusion — it happens all by itself.

Diffusion in Cells

You need to know a fair few underlined examples of how diffusion happens in our bodies. There's the small intestine, the lungs, the placenta and synapses. You also need to know how diffusion works in the leaves of plants (covered on page 60).

Small Food Molecules Can Diffuse into the Blood

1) Food is digested in the gut to break it down into pieces small enough to be absorbed into the blood by diffusion.

2) The absorption happens in the small intestine, after big molecules like starch, and proteins have been broken down into small ones like glucose and amino acids.

3) These molecules can diffuse into the blood from the small intestine because their concentration is higher than it is in the blood.

4) When the blood reaches cells that need these substances because their concentration is low, they can diffuse out easily from an area of higher concentration to an area of lower.

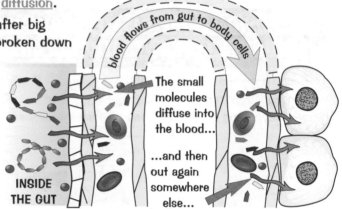

blood flows from gut to body cells

The small molecules diffuse into the blood...

...and then out again somewhere else...

INSIDE THE GUT

Villi in the Small Intestine Help with Diffusion

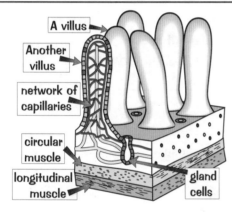

A villus

Another villus

network of capillaries

circular muscle

longitudinal muscle

gland cells

1) The small intestine is adapted for absorption of food.

2) It's very long, so there's time to break down and absorb all the food before it reaches the end.

3) There's a really big surface area for absorption, because the walls of the small intestine are covered in millions and millions of tiny little projections called villi.

4) Each cell on the surface of a villus also has its own microvilli — little projections that increase the surface area even more.

5) Villi have a single permeable layer of surface cells and a very good blood supply to assist quick absorption.

Alveoli Carry Out Gas Exchange in the Body

1) The lungs contain millions and millions of little air sacs called alveoli where gas exchange happens.

2) The blood passing next to the alveoli has just returned to the lungs from the rest of the body, so it contains lots of carbon dioxide and very little oxygen. Oxygen diffuses out of the alveolus (high concentration) into the blood (low concentration). Carbon dioxide diffuses out of the blood (high concentration) into the alveolus (low concentration) to be breathed out.

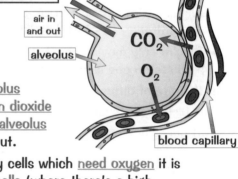

air in and out

alveolus

CO_2

O_2

blood capillary

3) When the blood reaches body cells which need oxygen it is released from the red blood cells (where there's a high concentration) and diffuses into the body cells (where the concentration is low).

4) At the same time, carbon dioxide diffuses out of the body cells (where there's a high concentration) into the blood (where there's a low concentration). It's then carried back to the lungs.

body cells

CO_2

O_2

blood capillary

Diffusion in Cells

Alveoli are Specialised for Gas Exchange

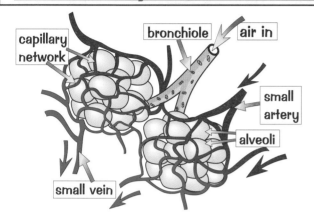

capillary network
bronchiole
air in
small artery
alveoli
small vein

The alveoli are an ideal exchange surface:

1) The huge number of microscopic alveoli gives the lungs an enormous surface area.

2) There's a moist lining for gases to dissolve in.

3) The alveoli have very thin walls — only one cell thick, so the gas doesn't have far to diffuse.

4) They have a great blood supply to maintain a high concentration gradient.

5) The walls are permeable — so gases can diffuse across easily.

Diffusion Also Happens in the Placenta

The placenta is the organ that connects mum and baby when a mammal is pregnant. The placenta is adapted for diffusion:

1) There are tiny projections (villi) in the placenta. These give a big surface area. They have capillaries inside containing the foetus's blood.

2) Spaces develop around the villi called sinuses, which become filled with the mother's blood.

3) This lets the mother's blood and the foetus's flow very close to each other so that there's a short distance for diffusion.

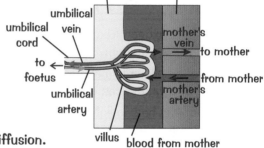

placenta   wall of womb
umbilical vein
umbilical cord
to foetus
umbilical artery
mother's vein
to mother
from mother
mother's artery
villus   blood from mother

4) Food and oxygen diffuse across from the mother's blood to the foetus's when the foetus needs them, from an area of higher concentration to an area of lower concentration.

5) Carbon dioxide and other wastes diffuse across the placenta in the other direction, from foetus to mum. You can probably fill in the high concentration to low concentration bit yourself by now.

And Finally, Diffusion Happens in Synapses

Hopefully you'll remember that neurones (nerves) are connected by synapses. A synapse is just a gap between the end of one neurone and the start of the next. You also need to know:

1) When a nerve impulse arrives at a synapse it triggers the release of a transmitter substance from the end of the neurone into the gap.

2) The transmitter substance diffuses across the gap between the neurones and binds to receptors on the end of the next neurone.

3) This stimulates a new nerve impulse in this neurone. The diffusion of the transmitter substance across the synapse has allowed the nerve impulse to jump the gap and continue on the other side.

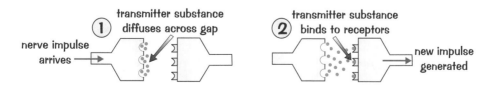

transmitter substance diffuses across gap
① nerve impulse arrives
transmitter substance binds to receptors
② new impulse generated

Don't worry — there's still diffusion in a leaf to look forward to...

...just in case you were getting upset at the thought of not hearing any more about it. So that's five examples altogether (including the leaf, see p.60). The process of diffusion is the same in each case.

42

Functions of the Blood

Blood is very useful stuff. It's a big transport system for moving things around the body. The <u>blood cells</u> do good work too. The <u>red blood cells</u> are responsible for transporting <u>oxygen</u> about, and they carry 100 times more than could be moved just dissolved in the plasma. And as for the white blood cells...

Plasma *is the Liquid Bit of Blood*

It's basically blood minus the blood cells (see below). Plasma is a pale yellow liquid which <u>carries just about everything</u> that needs transporting around your body:

1) <u>Red</u> and <u>white blood cells</u> (see below) and <u>platelets (used in clotting)</u>.

2) <u>Water</u>.

3) Digested food products like <u>glucose</u> and <u>amino acids</u> from the gut to all the body cells.

4) <u>Carbon dioxide</u> from the body cells to the lungs.

5) <u>Urea</u> from the liver to the kidneys (where it's removed in the urine).

6) <u>Hormones</u> — these act like chemical messengers.

7) <u>Antibodies</u> and <u>antitoxins</u> produced by the white blood cells (see below).

Red Blood Cells *Have the Job of Carrying Oxygen*

They transport <u>oxygen</u> from the <u>lungs</u> to <u>all</u> the cells in the body. The <u>structure</u> of a red blood cell is adapted to its <u>function</u>:

1) Red blood cells are <u>small</u> and have a <u>biconcave shape</u> (which is a posh way of saying they look a little bit like doughnuts, see diagram below) to give a <u>large surface area</u> for <u>absorbing</u> and <u>releasing oxygen</u>.

2) They contain <u>haemoglobin</u>, which is what gives blood its <u>colour</u> — it contains a lot of <u>iron</u>. In the lungs, haemoglobin <u>reacts with oxygen</u> to become <u>oxyhaemoglobin</u>. In body tissues the reverse reaction happens to <u>release oxygen to the cells</u>.

3) Red blood cells don't have a <u>nucleus</u> — this frees up <u>space</u> for more haemoglobin, so they can carry more oxygen.

4) Red blood cells are very <u>flexible</u>. This means they can easily pass through the <u>tiny capillaries</u> (see next page).

White Blood Cells *are Used to Fight Disease*

1) Their main role is <u>defence against disease</u>.

2) They produce <u>antibodies</u> to fight microbes.

3) They produce <u>antitoxins</u> to neutralise the toxins produced by microbes.

4) They have a <u>flexible shape</u>, which helps them to <u>engulf</u> any micro-organisms they come across inside the body. Basically the white blood cell wraps around the micro-organism until it's <u>totally surrounded</u>, and then it <u>digests it</u> using enzymes.

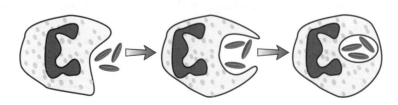

It's all blood, sweat and tears — kind of... *...without the sweat... or the tears... just the blood then... yep... anyway...*

The average human body contains about <u>six and a half pints</u> of blood altogether, and every single drop contains <u>millions</u> of cells. There are usually about 500 times more red blood cells than white.

Module B3 — Living and Growing

Circulatory System: Blood Vessels

Blood needs a good system to move it around the body — called the circulatory system.

Blood Vessels are Designed for Their Function

There are three different types of blood vessel:

> 1) ARTERIES — these carry the blood away from the heart.
> 2) CAPILLARIES — these are involved in the exchange of materials at the tissues.
> 3) VEINS — these carry the blood to the heart.

Arteries Carry Blood Under Pressure

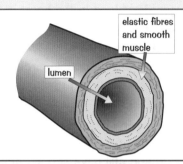

1) The heart pumps the blood out at high pressure so the artery walls are strong and elastic.

2) The walls are thick compared to the size of the hole down the middle (the "lumen" — silly name!). They contain thick layers of muscle to make them strong.

> Cholesterol is a fatty substance. Eating a diet high in saturated fat has been linked to high levels of cholesterol in the blood. You need some cholesterol for things like making cell membranes. But if you get too much cholesterol it starts to build up in your arteries. These form plaques in the wall of the lumen, which narrows the artery. This restricts the flow of blood — bad news for the part of the body the artery is supplying with food and oxygen. If an artery supplying the heart or brain is affected, it can cause a heart attack or stroke.

Capillaries are Really Small

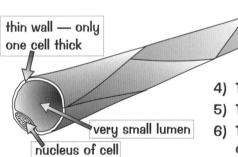

1) Arteries branch into capillaries.

2) Capillaries are really tiny — too small to see.

3) They carry the blood really close to every cell in the body to exchange substances with them.

4) They have permeable walls, so substances can diffuse in and out.

5) They supply food and oxygen, and take away wastes like CO_2.

6) Their walls are usually only one cell thick. This increases the rate of diffusion by decreasing the distance over which it occurs.

Veins Take Blood Back to the Heart

1) Capillaries eventually join up to form veins.

2) The blood is at lower pressure in the veins so the walls don't need to be as thick as artery walls.

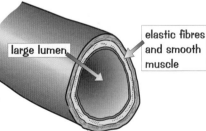

3) They have a bigger lumen than arteries to help the blood flow despite the lower pressure.

4) They also have valves to help keep the blood flowing in the right direction.

Learn this page — don't struggle in vein...

Here's an interesting fact for you — your body contains about 60 000 miles of blood vessels. That's about six times the distance from London to Sydney in Australia. Of course, capillaries are really tiny, which is how there can be such a big length — they can only be seen with a microscope.

Circulatory System: The Heart

Blood doesn't just move around the body <u>on its own</u>, of course. It needs a <u>pump</u>.

Mammals Have a Double Circulatory System

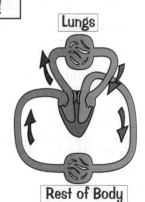

1) The first one connects the <u>heart</u> to the <u>lungs</u>. <u>Deoxygenated</u> blood is pumped to the <u>lungs</u> to take in <u>oxygen</u>. The blood then <u>returns</u> to the heart.

2) The second one connects the <u>heart</u> to the <u>rest of the body</u>. The <u>oxygenated</u> blood in the heart is pumped out to the <u>body</u>. It <u>gives up</u> its oxygen, and then the <u>deoxygenated</u> blood <u>returns</u> to the heart to be pumped out to the <u>lungs</u> again.

3) Not all animals have a double circulatory system — <u>fish</u> don't, for example. So why can't mammals just pump the blood out <u>through the lungs</u> and then on to the rest of the body?

4) Well, returning the blood to the <u>heart</u> after it's picked up oxygen at the <u>lungs</u> means it can be pumped out around the body with <u>much greater force</u>. This is needed so the blood can get to <u>every last tissue</u> in the body and <u>still</u> have enough push left to flow <u>back to the heart</u> through the veins.

Learn This Diagram of the Heart with All Its Labels

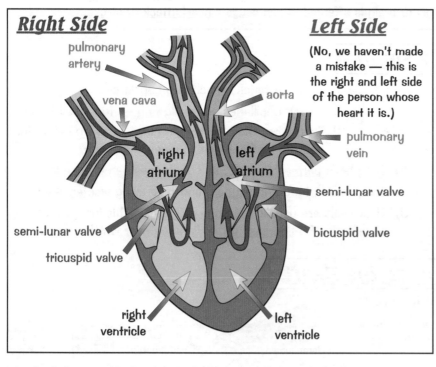

1) The <u>right atrium</u> of the heart receives <u>deoxygenated</u> blood from the <u>body</u> (through the <u>vena cava</u>).

(The plural of atrium is atria.)

2) The deoxygenated blood moves through to the <u>right ventricle</u>, which pumps it to the <u>lungs</u> (via the <u>pulmonary artery</u>).

3) The <u>left atrium</u> receives <u>oxygenated</u> blood from the <u>lungs</u> (through the <u>pulmonary vein</u>).

4) The oxygenated blood then moves through to the <u>left ventricle</u>, which pumps it out round the <u>whole body</u> (via the <u>aorta</u>).

5) The <u>left</u> ventricle has a much <u>thicker wall</u> than the <u>right</u> ventricle. It needs more <u>muscle</u> because it has to pump blood around the <u>whole body</u>, whereas the right ventricle only has to pump it to the <u>lungs</u>.

6) The <u>semi-lunar</u>, <u>tricuspid</u> and <u>bicuspid valves</u> prevent the <u>backflow</u> of blood.

Okay — let's get to the heart of the matter...

The human heart beats <u>100 000 times a day</u> on average. You can feel a <u>pulse</u> in your wrist or neck (where the vessels are close to the surface). This is the <u>blood</u> being pushed along by another beat. Doctors use a <u>stethoscope</u> to listen to your heart — it's actually the <u>valves closing</u> that they hear.

Module B3 — Living and Growing

Replacement Hearts

Heart disease is one of the main killer diseases of the Western world, but nowadays many people with defective hearts can have surgery to put the problems right.

You Can Just Replace Parts of the Heart

The heart has a pacemaker — a group of cells which determines how fast it beats. If this stops working properly the heartbeat becomes irregular, which can be dangerous. The pacemaker then needs to be replaced with an artificial one. Defective heart valves can also be replaced — either with valves from animals, or with artificial, mechanical valves.

Or You Can Get a Heart Transplant...

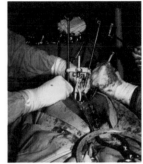

In extreme cases, the whole heart can be removed and replaced by another one from a human donor — this is called a transplant. It involves major surgery and a lifetime course of drugs and medical care. They're only done on patients whose hearts are so damaged that the problems can't be solved in any other way.

...But You Need a Donor

One of the major problems in getting a heart transplant is a shortage of donors.
To be a heart donor, the person must meet these criteria:

1) Relatively young (under 45), so that the heart is as fit and healthy as possible.

2) Tissues must be a close match to those of the patient, or the heart's likely to be rejected (see below).

3) Body weight must be similar to the patient needing the transplant, so the heart is a good 'fit'.

4) Hearts stay usable for no more than 6 hours outside the body — so the donor must have only very recently died or their heart must still be working (i.e. the patient is 'brain dead', but they've been kept 'alive' artificially so their heart hasn't actually stopped yet).

5) Close relatives must give permission.

> **TRANSPLANTS CAN BE REJECTED** One of the main problems with heart transplants is that the patient's immune system often recognises the new heart as 'foreign' and attacks it — this is called rejection. Doctors use drugs that suppress the patient's immune system to help stop the donor heart being rejected, but that leaves the patient more vulnerable to infections. Rejection can also occur with replacement heart valves from animals.

Mechanical Parts aren't Usually Rejected by the Body

1) The main advantage of using artificial parts (valves and pacemakers) is that rejection isn't normally a problem. They're usually made from metals or plastics, which the body can't recognise as foreign in the same way as it does with living tissue.

2) Pacemakers do need a battery, but this is very small and is inserted under the skin. It lasts for about ten years and is easily replaced.

3) Artificial valves need more major surgery and don't work quite as well as healthy natural ones — the blood doesn't flow through them as smoothly, which can cause blood clots and lead to strokes. The patient has to take drugs to thin their blood and make sure this doesn't happen, which can cause problems if they're hurt in an accident.

4) Replacing a valve is a much less drastic procedure than a transplant, and inserting a pacemaker only involves an overnight stay in hospital.

Pity they can't fit me in for a brain transplant before the exam...

The first successful heart transplant took place in South Africa in 1967. They can transplant loads of stuff nowadays — kidneys, lungs, liver, pancreas, corneas, small intestine... but they all need donors.

Multiplying Cells

Cell division — pretty important if you're planning on being bigger than an amoeba. Which I am, one day.

Being Multi-cellular Has Some Important Advantages

There's nothing wrong with single-celled organisms — they're pretty successful. Bacteria, for example, aren't in danger of extinction any time soon. But there are some big advantages in being multi-cellular, and so some organisms have cleverly evolved that way. Here are some advantages you should know:

1) A single large cell has a smaller surface area to volume ratio than lots of small cells do. This reduces the organism's ability to move substances in and out of the cell.

2) Being multi-cellular means you can be bigger. This is great because it means you can travel further, get your nutrients in a variety of different ways, fewer things can eat or squash you, etc.

3) Being multi-cellular allows for cell differentiation. Instead of being just one cell that has to do everything, you can have different types of cells that do different jobs. Your cells can be specially adapted for their particular jobs, e.g. taking in oxygen in the blood, reacting to light in the eyes.

4) This means multi-cellular organisms can be more complex — they can have specialised organs, different shapes and behaviour — and so can be adapted specifically to their particular environment.

Mitosis Makes New Cells for Growth and Repair

"Mitosis is when a cell reproduces itself by splitting to form two identical offspring."

This happens in the body when you want identical cells — e.g. when you want to grow and you need lots of the same type of cell, when you need to repair cells that have been damaged or when you need to replace worn-out cells. The important thing to understand in mitosis is what happens to the DNA.

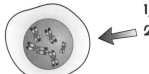

1) Before mitosis starts, the DNA in the cell is replicated (see p.35).

2) Then at the beginning of mitosis, the DNA coils into double-armed chromosomes. These arms are exact duplicates of each other — they contain exactly the same DNA.

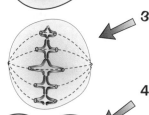

3) The chromosomes line up at the centre of the cell, and then cell fibres pull them apart. One arm of each chromosome goes to one end of the cell, and the other goes to the opposite end. Membranes form around each of these two different sets of chromosomes.

4) The cytoplasm divides, and you get two new cells containing exactly the same genetic material.

5) And that's mitosis. You've ended up with two new cells with exactly the same genetic information as each other. Before these can divide again, the DNA has to replicate itself to give each chromosome two arms again.

The Other Type of Cell Division is Meiosis

1) Reproductive cells undergo meiosis to make gametes. These are the sex cells — eggs and sperm.

2) The body cells of mammals are diploid. This means that each of the organism's body cells has two copies of each chromosome in its nucleus — one from the organism's mum, and one from its dad.

3) But sex cells are haploid. They only have one copy of each chromosome (due to the way they divided — see next page). This is so that you can supply one sex cell from the mum (the egg) and one sex cell from the dad (the sperm) and still end up with the usual number of chromosomes in body cells.

Right — now that I have your undivided attention...

There's no denying mitosis and meiosis can seem tricky at first. But don't worry — just go through it slowly, one step at a time. Even if the exam's tomorrow. Panicking and rushing don't help at all.

Sexual Reproduction

People can look very similar to their mum and dad, often a good mix of the two. Here's why.

Meiosis Involves Two Divisions

1) Meiosis starts in exactly the same way as mitosis — the DNA replicates and curls up to form double-armed chromosomes (see previous page).

2) After replication the chromosomes arrange themselves into pairs. Humans have 23 pairs of chromosomes, that's 46 altogether. Both chromosomes in a pair contain information about the same features. One chromosome comes from your mum and one from your dad.

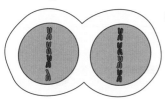

3) In the first division, these pairs split up — some of your dad's chromosomes go with some of your mum's chromosomes. In each of the two new cells, there are no pairs at all — just one of each of the 23 different types. So each new cell has a mixture of your mum's and your dad's genes, but only half the usual number of chromosomes.

4) The second division of meiosis is like mitosis on the last page — each chromosome splits in half and one arm ends up in each new cell.

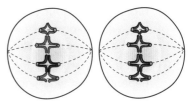

5) And that's meiosis. You've ended up with four new cells — two after the first division, and then each of those splits again. The cells are genetically different from each other because the genes all get shuffled up during meiosis and each gamete only gets half of them, at random.

Sexual Reproduction Creates Variation

> **SEXUAL REPRODUCTION** involves the fusion of male and female gametes (sex cells). Because there are **TWO** parents, the offspring contains a mixture of their parents' genes.

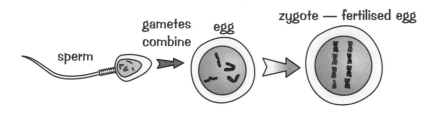

gametes combine — sperm — egg — zygote — fertilised egg

The offspring will have a mixture of the two sets of chromosomes, so it will inherit features from both parents. This is why sexual reproduction produces more variation than asexual reproduction.

Sperm Cells are Adapted for Their Function

The function of a sperm is to transport the male's DNA to the female's egg so that their DNA can combine.

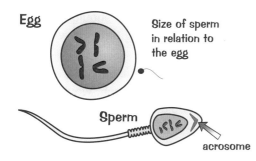

Egg — Size of sperm in relation to the egg — Sperm — acrosome

1) Sperm are small and have long tails so they can swim to the egg.

2) Sperm have lots of mitochondria (see page 35) to provide the energy needed to swim this distance.

3) Sperm also have an acrosome at the front of the 'head', where they store the enzymes they need to digest their way through the membrane of the egg cell.

4) They're produced in large numbers to increase the chance of fertilisation.

No sniggering in the back, please...

For many kids in year seven, the mere sight of a sperm is enough to convulse them in giggles. Those of them that don't think it's an innocent tadpole, anyway. But that's not the case for you lot. We hope.

Stem Cells and Differentiation

Plants and animals have different tactics for growth, but they both have stem cells.

Animals Stop Growing, Plants Can Grow Continuously

Plants and animals grow differently:

1) Animals tend to grow while they're young, and then they reach full growth and stop growing. Plants often grow continuously — even really old trees will keep putting out new branches.

2) In animals, growth happens by cell division, but in plants, growth in height is mainly due to cell enlargement (elongation) — cell division usually just happens in the tips of the roots and shoots.

Stem Cells Can Turn into Different Types of Cells

1) Differentiation is the process by which a cell changes to become specialised for its job. In most animal cells, the ability to differentiate is lost at an early stage, but lots of plant cells don't ever lose this ability.

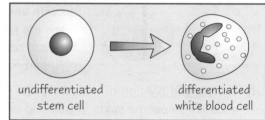

undifferentiated stem cell — differentiated white blood cell

2) Most cells in your body are specialised for a particular job. E.g. white blood cells are brilliant at fighting invaders but can't carry oxygen, like red blood cells.

3) Some cells are undifferentiated. They can develop into different types of cell, tissues and organs depending on what instructions they're given. These cells are called STEM CELLS.

4) Stem cells are found in early human embryos. They're exciting to doctors and medical researchers because they have the potential to turn into any kind of cell at all. This makes sense if you think about it — all the different types of cell found in a human being have to come from those few cells in the early embryo.

5) Adults also have stem cells, but they're only found in certain places, like bone marrow. These aren't as versatile as embryonic stem cells — they can't turn into any cell type at all, only certain ones.

Stem Cells May be Able to Cure Many Disorders

1) Medicine already uses stem cells to cure disease. For example, people with blood disorders (e.g. leukaemia and sickle cell anaemia) can be cured by bone marrow transplants. Bone marrow contains adult stem cells that turn into new blood cells (but nothing else) to replace faulty old ones.

2) Very early human embryos contain a lot of stem cells. Scientists can extract these and grow them. Researchers are trying to find out how to 'instruct' the cells to turn into useful cells, e.g. nerve cells to cure brain damage and spinal injuries, skin cells for skin grafts, etc.

3) Tissues derived from stem cells could be used for drug testing and development, reducing the need for animal testing.

Some People Are Against Stem Cell Research

1) Some people are against stem cell research because they feel that human embryos shouldn't be used for experiments since each one is a potential human life. Others think that curing patients who already exist and who are suffering is more important than the rights of embryos.

2) One fairly convincing argument in favour of this point of view is that the embryos used in the research are usually unwanted ones from fertility clinics which, if they weren't used for research, would probably just be destroyed. But of course, campaigners for the rights of embryos usually want this banned too.

3) Around the world, there are now 'stocks' of stem cells that scientists can use for their research. Some countries (e.g. the USA) won't fund research to make new stem cell stocks, but in the UK it's allowed as long as it follows strict guidelines.

But florists cell stems — and nobody complains about that...

Research has recently been done into getting stem cells from alternative sources. E.g. some researchers think it might be possible to get cells from umbilical cords to behave like embryonic stem cells.

Growth in Humans

Growth in humans is <u>more complicated</u> than just getting <u>born</u> and then getting <u>bigger</u>.

Growth Starts Well Before Birth

Mammals give birth to live young. So, the baby grows inside it's mothers womb until it reaches a stage where it can <u>survive</u> outside. This period is called <u>gestation</u> and its length <u>varies</u> in <u>different mammals</u>:

<u>Gestation length</u> is usually related to the <u>size</u> of the animal, but also to <u>how developed</u> it is at birth (e.g. kangaroo babies are born relatively <u>undeveloped</u> and so the gestation period is quite <u>short</u>).

The human body <u>doesn't</u> grow <u>evenly</u> in the mother's womb or in early life. Certain organs grow <u>faster</u> than others, and the <u>fastest-growing</u> of all is the <u>brain</u>. This is because a large and well-developed brain gives humans a big <u>survival advantage</u> — it's our best tool for finding food, avoiding predators, etc.

The graphs show that, during the first year of life, a baby's <u>head size</u> increases <u>in proportion</u> with its <u>body weight</u> (the <u>slope</u> of both graphs is about the <u>same</u>). <u>Head growth</u> is actually responsible for much of the <u>weight increase</u> in the baby. Doctors <u>monitor</u> the baby's <u>weight</u> and <u>head circumference</u>. The actual values are not as important as the <u>rate</u> of growth. If the baby is growing too <u>slowly</u>, or if the head is relatively too <u>large</u> or <u>small</u>, it can alert the doctor to possible <u>development problems</u>.

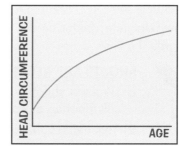
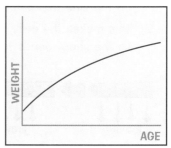

The Human Life Span Has Five Stages

During a normal life span, everyone passes through these <u>five stages</u>. Some of the stages have a <u>clearly defined</u> beginning and end, while others are a bit more vague.

STAGE	DESCRIPTION
<u>Infancy</u>	Roughly the <u>first year</u> of life. Time of rapid growth, child begins to walk.
<u>Childhood</u>	Period between <u>infancy</u> and <u>puberty</u>. Development of the brain.
<u>Adolescence</u>	Begins with <u>puberty</u> and continues until body development and growth are <u>complete</u>.
<u>Maturity/adulthood</u>	Period between <u>adolescence</u> and <u>old age</u>. Cell division for growth stops.
<u>Old age</u>	Usually considered to be between <u>age 65</u> and <u>death</u>.

You Need to be Able to Interpret Data on Human Growth

In exams, you may be asked to <u>interpret</u> human growth data. This will usually show growth over a period of time. Be really careful to note whether the data shows <u>actual growth</u> or <u>growth rate</u> (speed of growth).

If it shows <u>actual growth</u>, you can judge the rate of growth by looking at the <u>slope</u> of the graph. In this growth <u>rate</u> example graph, you might be asked to describe <u>changes</u> in the rate of growth, or note <u>key points</u> (e.g. there's a sudden <u>growth spurt</u> at the beginning of puberty).

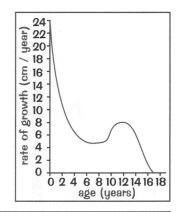

I'm growing rather sick of this topic...

Listen, you think <u>you're</u> sick of reading these lame jokes? Just think how <u>I</u> feel, having to make them up.

Growth in Plants

Plants <u>don't</u> just grow randomly. Plant hormones make sure they grow in the <u>right direction</u>.

Auxins <u>are</u> Plant <u>Growth Hormones</u>

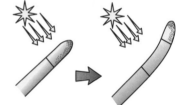

1) <u>Auxins</u> are <u>plant hormones</u> which control <u>growth</u> at the <u>tips</u> of <u>shoots</u> and <u>roots</u>.

2) Auxin is produced in the <u>tips</u> and <u>diffuses backwards</u> to stimulate the <u>cell elongation process</u> which occurs in the cells <u>just behind</u> the tips.

3) If the tip of a shoot is <u>removed</u>, no auxin will be available and the shoot <u>stops growing</u>.

4) Auxins are involved in the responses of plants to <u>light</u> and <u>gravity</u>.

Auxins <u>Change the Direction</u> of Root and Shoot Growth

You'll see below that extra auxin <u>promotes</u> growth in the <u>shoot</u> but actually <u>inhibits</u> growth in the <u>root</u> — but also note that this produces the <u>desired result</u> in <u>both cases</u>.

SHOOTS ARE POSITIVELY PHOTOTROPIC (grow towards light)

1) When a <u>shoot tip</u> is exposed to <u>light</u>, it accumulates <u>more auxin</u> on the side that's in the <u>shade</u> than the side that's in the light.

2) This makes the cells grow (elongate) <u>faster</u> on the <u>shaded side</u>, so the shoot bends <u>towards</u> the light.

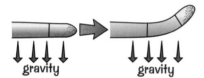

SHOOTS ARE NEGATIVELY GEOTROPIC (grow away from gravity)

1) When a <u>shoot</u> is growing sideways, <u>gravity</u> produces an unequal distribution of auxin in the tip, with <u>more auxin</u> on the <u>lower side</u>.

2) This causes the lower side to grow <u>faster</u>, bending the shoot <u>upwards</u>.

ROOTS ARE POSITIVELY GEOTROPIC (grow towards gravity)

1) A <u>root</u> growing sideways will also have more auxin on its <u>lower side</u>.

2) But in a root the <u>extra</u> auxin <u>inhibits</u> growth. This means the cells on <u>top</u> elongate faster, and the root bends <u>downwards</u>.

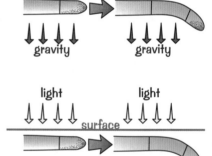

ROOTS ARE NEGATIVELY PHOTOTROPIC (grow away from light)

1) If a <u>root</u> starts being exposed to some <u>light</u>, it's probably getting near the <u>surface</u> — the <u>wrong direction</u> for a root to be going.

2) As in the shoot, <u>more auxin</u> accumulates on the more <u>shaded</u> side. The auxin <u>inhibits</u> cell elongation on the shaded side, so the root bends <u>downwards</u>, back into the ground.

Experiments <u>Have Shown</u> How Auxins Work

The two experiments illustrated show that auxins are <u>produced</u> in the <u>tip</u> of the plant (experiment 1) and cause <u>bending</u> by <u>building up</u> on the <u>shaded side</u> of the shoot (experiment 2).

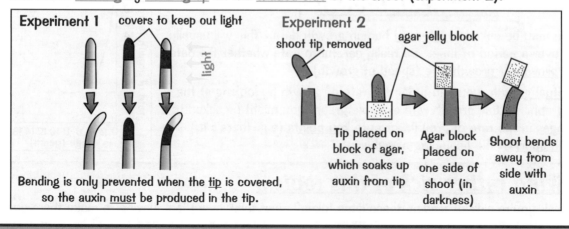

Experiment 1 — covers to keep out light — light

Bending is only prevented when the <u>tip</u> is covered, so the auxin <u>must</u> be produced in the tip.

Experiment 2 — shoot tip removed — agar jelly block

Tip placed on block of agar, which soaks up auxin from tip

Agar block placed on one side of shoot (in darkness)

Shoot bends away from side with auxin

Commercial Use of Plant Hormones

Plant hormones can be extracted and used by people, or artificial copies can be made. They can then be used to do all kinds of useful things, including killing weeds, growing cuttings and ripening fruit.

1) As Selective Weedkillers

1) Most weeds growing in fields of crops or in a lawn are broad-leaved, in contrast to grasses and cereals which have very narrow leaves.
2) Selective weedkillers have been developed from plant growth hormones which only affect the broad-leaved plants.
3) They totally disrupt their normal growth patterns, which soon kills them, whilst leaving the grass and crops untouched.

Unhappy weeds

2) Growing from Cuttings with Rooting Powder

1) A cutting is part of a plant that has been cut off it, like the end of a branch with a few leaves on it.
2) Normally, if you stick cuttings in the soil they won't grow, but if you add rooting powder, which contains a plant growth hormone, they will produce roots rapidly and start growing as new plants.
3) This enables growers to produce lots of clones (exact copies, see page 57) of a really good plant very quickly.

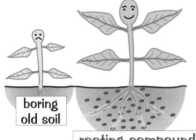
boring old soil
rooting compound

3) Controlling the Ripening of Fruit

1) The ripening of fruits can be controlled either while they are still on the plant, or during transport to the shops.
2) This allows the fruit to be picked while it's still unripe (and therefore firmer and less easily damaged).
3) Ripening hormone is then added and the fruit will ripen on the way to the supermarket and be perfect just as it reaches the shelves.

4) Controlling Dormancy

1) Lots of seeds won't germinate (start growing) until they've been through certain conditions (e.g. a period of cold or of dryness). This is called dormancy.
2) Another hormone called gibberellin is what breaks this dormancy and allows the seeds to germinate.
3) Commercial growers can treat seeds with gibberellin to make them germinate at times of year when they wouldn't normally. It also helps to make sure all the seeds in a batch germinate at the same time.

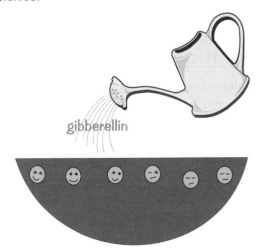
gibberellin

You will ripen when I SAY you can ripen — and NOT BEFORE...

If you want some fruit to ripen, put them into a paper bag with a banana. The banana releases a ripening hormone called ethene which causes the fruit to ripen. Bad apples also release lots of ethene. Unfortunately this means if you've got one bad apple in a barrel, you'll soon have lots of bad apples.

Module B3 — Living and Growing

Mutation

Mutations are really common — but sadly, they hardly ever give any of us superpowers.

Gene Mutations are Changes to Genes

A MUTATION is a change in the DNA base sequence.

1) There are several things that cause <u>mutations</u> — they even occur <u>spontaneously</u>.

2) These things change the <u>base sequence</u> of the DNA (see p.35). If this change becomes <u>permanent</u> (the DNA replicates before it's fixed) it becomes a <u>mutation</u>.

3) If the mutation occurs within a gene, it means that when the <u>code</u> is read in order to make <u>proteins</u>, you end up with either a <u>different</u> protein or <u>no</u> protein at all.

Most Mutations are Harmful

1) Making the wrong protein or no protein at all can be a bit of a <u>disaster</u> — especially if the protein is an <u>important enzyme</u> or something.

2) If a mutation occurs in <u>reproductive cells</u>, then the offspring might <u>develop abnormally</u> or <u>die</u> at an early stage of their development.

3) If a mutation occurs in <u>body cells</u>, the mutant cells can sometimes start to <u>multiply</u> in an <u>uncontrolled</u> way and <u>invade</u> other parts of the body. This is what we know as <u>cancer</u>.

Some Mutations are Beneficial, Giving Us Evolution

1) Occasionally, a different protein might be produced after a mutation that actually <u>benefits</u> the organism — the new protein is an <u>improvement</u> on the one it was supposed to be.

2) This gives the organism a <u>survival advantage</u> over the rest of the population. It passes on the mutated DNA to its <u>offspring</u>, and they survive better too, so soon the mutation becomes <u>common</u> in the population. This is <u>natural selection</u> and <u>evolution</u> at work. A good example is a mutation in a bacterium that makes it <u>resistant to antibiotics</u>, so the mutant gene <u>lives on</u>, creating a <u>resistant "strain"</u> of bacteria.

3) <u>Blue budgies</u> appeared suddenly as a <u>mutation</u> amongst yellow budgies. This is a good example of a <u>neutral effect</u>. It didn't <u>harm</u> its chances of survival and so it <u>remained</u> in the population (and at one stage, every grandma in Britain had one).

Radiation and Certain Chemicals Cause Mutations

Mutations occur 'naturally', caused by 'natural' <u>background radiation</u> (from the Sun, and rocks etc.) or just by the laws of <u>chance</u> that every now and then the DNA doesn't quite <u>copy itself</u> properly. However the chance of mutation is <u>increased</u> if you're exposed to:

1) <u>ionising radiation</u>, including <u>X-rays</u> and <u>ultraviolet light</u> (which are the <u>highest-frequency</u> parts of the EM spectrum), together with radiation from <u>radioactive substances</u>. For each of these examples, the <u>greater the dose</u> of radiation, the <u>greater the chance</u> of mutation.

2) certain <u>chemicals</u> which are known to cause mutations. Such chemicals are called <u>mutagens</u>. If the mutations produce <u>cancer</u> then the chemicals are often called <u>carcinogens</u>. <u>Cigarette smoke</u> contains chemical mutagens (or carcinogens).

Run, run, it's a mutant! Run from the terrible blue budgie...

All living organisms have experienced <u>mutation</u> at some point in their <u>evolutionary history</u>. That's why we don't all look the <u>same</u>. They're not usually as dramatic as turning you into a human torch either.

Selective Breeding

'Selective breeding' sounds like it has the potential to be a tricky topic, but it's actually dead simple.
You take the best plants or animals and breed them together to get the best possible offspring. That's it.

Selective Breeding is Very Simple

Organisms are selectively bred to develop the best features, which are things like:

    A) Maximum yield of meat, milk, grain etc.

    B) Good health and disease resistance.

    C) In animals, other qualities like temperament, speed, fertility, good mothering skills, etc.

    D) In plants, other qualities like attractive flowers, nice smell, etc.

Selective breeding is also called artificial selection, because humans artificially select the plants or animals that are going to breed and have their genes remain in the population, according to what we want from them. This is the basic process involved in selective breeding:

1) From your existing stock select the ones which have the best characteristics.

2) Breed them with each other.

3) Select the best of the offspring, and breed them together.

4) Continue this process over several generations, and the desirable trait gets stronger and stronger. In farming, this will give the farmer gradually better and better yields.

The Main Drawback is a Reduction in the Gene Pool

1) The main problem with selective breeding is that it reduces the number of different alleles (forms of a gene) in a population because the farmer keeps breeding from the "best" animals or plants — the same ones all the time.

2) There's more chance of the organisms developing genetic disorders when the gene pool is limited like this. This is because lots of these conditions are recessive — you need two alleles to be the same for it to have an effect. Related individuals are more likely to share the same alleles.

3) There can also be serious problems if a new disease appears, because there's little variety in the population. All the stock are closely related to each other, so if one of them is going to be killed by a new disease, the others are also likely to succumb to it.

| Selective Breeding | → | Reduction in the number of different alleles (genes) | → | Less chance of any resistant alleles being present in the population | → | Nothing to selectively breed a new strain from |

I use the same genes all the time too — they flatter my hips...

Selective breeding's not a new thing. People have been doing it for yonks. That's how we ended up with something like a poodle from a wolf. Somebody thought 'I really like this small, woolly, yappy wolf — I'll breed it with this other one'. And after thousands of generations, we got poodles. Hurrah.

Genetic Engineering

Genetic engineering — playing around with genes. Cool.

Genetic Engineering is Great — Hopefully

This is a young science with <u>exciting possibilities</u> (but <u>potential dangers</u> too). The basic idea is to move sections of <u>DNA</u> (genes) from one organism to another so that it produces <u>useful biological products</u>.

You need to be able to explain some of the <u>advantages</u> and <u>risks</u> involved in genetic engineering.

1) The main <u>advantage</u> is that you can produce organisms with <u>new</u> and very <u>useful</u> features. There are some examples of this below — make sure you learn them.

2) The main <u>risk</u> is that the inserted gene might have <u>unexpected harmful effects</u>. For example, genes are often inserted into <u>bacteria</u> so they produce useful <u>products</u>. If these bacteria <u>mutated</u> and became <u>pathogenic</u> (disease-causing), the <u>foreign genes</u> might make them more <u>harmful</u> and <u>unpredictable</u>. People also worry about the engineered DNA '<u>escaping</u>' — e.g. <u>weeds</u> could gain rogue genes from a crop that's had genes for <u>herbicide resistance</u> inserted into it. Then they'd be unstoppable. Eeek.

Genetic Engineering Involves These Important Stages:

1) First the <u>gene</u> that's responsible for producing the <u>desirable characteristic</u> is selected (say the gene for human insulin).

2) It's then '<u>cut</u>' from the DNA using <u>enzymes</u>, and <u>isolated</u>.

3) The useful gene is <u>inserted</u> into the <u>host DNA</u> of a bacterium.

4) The host bacterium is now <u>cultivated</u> and soon there are <u>millions</u> of similar bacteria all producing, say, <u>human insulin</u>.

Learn These Three Examples of Genetic Engineering:

1) In some parts of the world, the population relies heavily on <u>rice</u> for food. In these areas, <u>vitamin A deficiency</u> can be a problem, because rice doesn't contain much of this vitamin, and other sources are <u>scarce</u>. Genetic engineering has allowed scientists to take a <u>gene</u> that controls <u>beta-carotene production</u> from <u>carrot plants</u>, and put it into <u>rice plants</u>. Humans can then change the beta-carotene into Vitamin A. Problem solved.

2) The gene for <u>human insulin production</u> has been put into <u>bacteria</u>. These are <u>cultured</u> in a <u>fermenter</u>, and the human insulin is simply <u>extracted</u> from the medium as they produce it. Great.

3) Some plants have <u>resistance</u> to things like <u>herbicides</u>, <u>frost damage</u> and <u>disease</u>. Unfortunately, it's not always the plants we <u>want to grow</u> that have these features. But now, thanks to genetic engineering, we can <u>cut out</u> the gene responsible and stick it into <u>any useful plant we like</u>. Splendid.

There's Moral and Ethical Issues Involved

All this is nice, but you need to be able to weigh up these <u>benefits</u> against the <u>moral and ethical issues</u>:

1) Some people think it's <u>wrong</u> to genetically engineer other organisms purely for <u>human benefit</u>. This is a particular problem in the genetic engineering of <u>animals</u>, especially if the animal <u>suffers</u> as a result.

2) People worry that we won't <u>stop</u> at engineering <u>plants</u> and <u>animals</u>. Those who can afford it might decide which characteristics they want their <u>children</u> to have, creating a '<u>genetic underclass</u>'.

3) The <u>evolutionary consequences</u> of genetic engineering are <u>unknown</u>, so some people think it's <u>irresponsible</u> to carry on when we're not sure what the <u>impact</u> on <u>future generations</u> might be.

4) There are concerns about '<u>playing God</u>', and meddling with things that should be left well alone.

Barry played God in the school nativity — I was a sheep...

You can do great things with genetic engineering. But some people worry that we <u>don't know enough</u> about it, or that some <u>maniac</u> is going to come along and combine Cherie Blair with a grapefruit. Possibly.

Cloning: Embryo Transplants

Eeek, cloning. People get even more worked up about this than they do about genetic engineering. But embryo transplants are pretty widely used now — people don't get as upset when it's just farm animals.

Cloning is Making an Exact Copy of Another Organism

Learn this definition of clones:

Clones are genetically identical organisms.

Clones occur naturally in both plants and animals. Identical twins are clones of each other.
These days clones are very much a part of the high-tech farming industry.

You Need to Know About Embryo Transplants in Cows

Normally, farmers only breed from their best cows and bulls. However, such traditional methods would only allow the prize cow to produce one new offspring each year. These days the whole process has been transformed using embryo transplants:

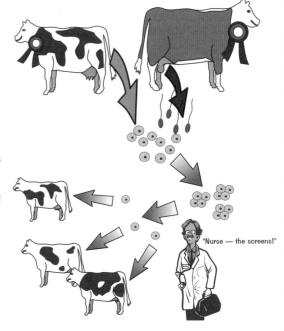

"Nurse — the screens!"

1) Sperm are taken from the prize bull. They can also be frozen and used at a later date.

2) Selected prize cows are given hormones to make them produce lots of eggs.

3) The cows are then artificially inseminated.

4) The fertilised eggs divide to give a ball of genetically identical cells which develops into an embryo.

5) The embryos are taken from the prize cows. Their sex is checked and they're screened for genetic defects.

6) The embryos are then split into separate cells before any cells become specialised. Each cell grows into a new embryo which is a clone of the original one.

7) The offspring are clones of each other, NOT clones of their parents.

8) These embryos are implanted into other cows, called 'surrogate mothers', where they grow. They can also be frozen and used at a later date.

Advantages of Embryo Transplants — Hundreds of Ideal Offspring

a) Hundreds of "ideal" offspring can be produced every year from the best bull and cow.

b) The original prize cow can keep producing prize eggs all year round.

Disadvantages — Reduced Gene Pool

The main problem is that the same alleles keep appearing (and many others are lost).
So there's a greater risk of genetic disorders (see page 19), and a disease could wipe out an entire population if there are no resistant alleles.

Thank goodness they didn't do that with my little brother...

It seems strange that you can pull apart a growing embryo and not harm it. But at that stage, the cells are all the same — they haven't started to differentiate into different cells with different jobs to do yet. So if you can separate them gently enough that the cells aren't damaged, they keep dividing quite happily.

Adult Cloning

Ah, Dolly the sheep. It seems a long time ago now, but she was the first mammal cloned from an adult cell. She was born in 1996, the only success of 277 attempts by the team who created her.

Cloning an Adult is Done by Transplanting a Cell Nucleus

The first mammal to be successfully cloned from an adult cell was a sheep called "Dolly".
This is the method that was used to produce Dolly:

1) The nucleus of a sheep's egg cell was removed — this left the egg cell without any genetic information.

2) Another nucleus was inserted in its place. This was a diploid nucleus from an udder cell of a different sheep (the one being cloned) and had all its genetic information.

3) The cell was stimulated so that it started dividing by mitosis, as if it was a normal fertilised egg.

4) The dividing cell was implanted into the uterus of another sheep to develop until it was ready to be born.

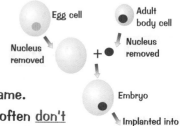

5) The result was Dolly, a clone of the sheep from which the udder cell came.

There are risks with cloning. Embryos formed by cloning from adult cells often don't develop normally. There had been many failed attempts at producing a clone from an adult before the success with Dolly.

There are Both Benefits and Risks Involved in Cloning

There are many possible benefits of cloning:

1) Animals that can produce medicines in their milk could be cloned. Researchers have managed to transfer human genes that produce useful proteins into sheep and cows, so that they can produce, for example, the blood clotting agent factor VIII used for treating haemophilia. With cloning, you only need to transfer the genes once, and then you could clone the animal as many times as you liked.

2) Animals (probably pigs) that have organs suitable for organ transplantation into humans (xenotransplantation) could be developed by genetic engineering and then cloned in the same way.

3) The study of animal clones and cloned cells could lead to greater understanding of the development of the embryo and of ageing and age-related disorders.

4) Cloning could be used to help preserve endangered species.

But there are risks too:

1) There is some evidence that cloned animals might not be as healthy as normal ones.

2) Cloning is a new science and it might have consequences that we're not yet aware of.

3) People are worried that humans might be produced by cloning if research continues.

Cloning Humans is a Possibility — with a Lot of Ethical Issues

As the technology used to clone mammals improves, it becomes more and more likely that humans could one day be cloned as well. However, there are still enormous difficulties to be overcome, and it might well involve women willing to donate hundreds of eggs. There would have to be lots of surrogate pregnancies, probably with high rates of miscarriage and stillbirth. The problems scientists have had with other mammals (see below) have shown that the human clones produced could well be unhealthy and die prematurely. There are also worries that if we clone humans we will be 'playing God', and meddling with things we don't fully understand. Even if a healthy clone were produced, it might be psychologically damaged by the knowledge that it's just a clone of another human being.

A whole lamb from a single cell? Pull the udder one...

Since Dolly, scientists have successfully cloned all kinds of mammals including goats, cows, mice, pigs, cats, rabbits, horses and dogs. Many of these clones suffered health problems and died young — Dolly seemed normal, but died aged just six (when the breed has a life expectancy of 11-12).

Cloning Plants: Asexual Reproduction

Many Plants Produce Clones — All by Themselves

This means they produce <u>exact genetic copies</u> of themselves without involving another plant.

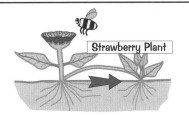

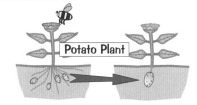

1) <u>Strawberry plants</u> produce runners.

2) <u>Tubers</u> grow on plants like <u>potatoes</u> and give clones of the parent plant.

Gardeners are familiar with taking <u>cuttings</u> from good parent plants, and then planting them to produce <u>identical copies</u> (clones) of the parent plant. Cloning plants is <u>easier</u> than cloning animals because many plant cells keep their ability to <u>differentiate</u> (see page 48) — animal cells <u>lose this</u> at an early stage.

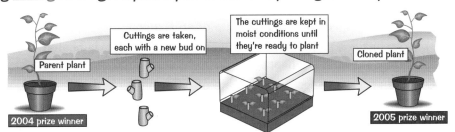

Commercial Cloning Often Involves Tissue Culture

1) First you choose the plant you want to clone based on its <u>characteristics</u> — e.g. a beautiful flower, a good fruit crop.

2) You <u>remove</u> a small amount of <u>tissue</u> from the <u>parent plant</u>. Because you only need a <u>tiny amount</u>, you can remove tissue from <u>several points</u> to give <u>several clones</u>. You get the best results if you take tissue from <u>fast-growing root and shoot tips</u>.

3) You grow the tissue in a medium containing <u>nutrients</u> and <u>growth hormones</u>. This is done under <u>aseptic</u> (sterile) conditions to prevent growth of <u>microbes</u> that could harm the plants.

4) As the tissues produce shoots and roots they can be moved to <u>potting compost</u> to carry on growing.

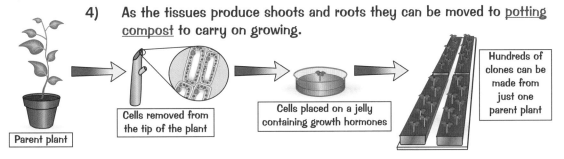

Commercial Use of Cloned Plants Has Pros and Cons

1) You can be <u>fairly sure</u> of the characteristics of the plant because it'll be <u>genetically identical</u> to the parent — so you'll only get <u>good ones</u>, and won't waste time and money growing duds.

2) It's possible to <u>mass-produce</u> plants that are <u>hard</u> to grow from scratch.

3) But, if the plants suffer from a <u>disease</u> or start doing badly because of a change in <u>environment</u>, they'll <u>all</u> have the same problems because they all have the same genes.

4) And there are the usual problems with lack of <u>genetic variation</u> (see page 53).

Stop cloning around — just learn it...

<u>Plants</u> are much better at being cloned than mammals are. They don't start <u>dropping dead</u> or having <u>health problems</u>, they just get on with it. And nobody seems that bothered about <u>ethics</u> when it's a tulip.

Revision Summary for Module B3

Well, just look at this — it's your first Revision Summary page. There's one of these little fellas at the end of every section, and my, they're a right bundle of laughs. No really, they're hilarious. Just look at question one there — "Where in a cell does respiration happen?" HAAAAH HAR HAR HAR. Good one.

1) Where in a cell does respiration happen?
2) What is a nucleotide?
3) How can DNA fingerprinting be used in forensic science?
4) As part of the DNA fingerprinting method, DNA is cut into fragments. How is this done?
5) The DNA is then suspended in a gel and an electric current is passed through it.
   How does this separate out the DNA fragments?
6) What is transamination?
7) What name is given to biological catalysts?
8) What happens at the active site of an enzyme?
9) An enzyme with an optimum temperature of 37 °C is heated to 60 °C.
   Suggest what will happen to the enzyme.
10) What three things does the rate of diffusion depend on?
11) Give three ways that the small intestine is adapted for absorption.
12) Why does oxygen enter the blood in the alveoli, and leave it when it reaches a respiring tissue?
13) Name two substances that diffuse through the placenta from the foetus to the mother.
14) Name six things that blood plasma transports around the body.
15) Name the substance formed in red blood cells when haemoglobin reacts with oxygen.
16) Why do arteries need very muscular, elastic walls?
17) Explain how capillaries are adapted to their function.
18) Name the blood vessel that joins to the right ventricle of the heart. Where does it take the blood?
19) Why does the left ventricle have a thicker wall than the right ventricle?
20) What must doctors consider when deciding if someone is a suitable donor for a heart transplant?
21) How many cells are produced after a mitotic division? Are they genetically identical?
22) How many cells are produced after a meiotic division? Are they genetically identical?
23) Give three ways that sperm cells are adapted for their function.
24) Describe two differences in the way plant cells and animal cells grow and develop.
25) Explain how stem cells could be used to cure a serious spinal injury.
26) List the five stages of growth seen in a normal human life span.
27) What are auxins?
28) Shoots are negatively geotropic. How are auxins responsible for this?
29) Give three ways that plant growth hormones are used commercially.
30) Why are mutations in an organism's DNA often harmful to that organism?
31) Give two things that increase the rate of mutation if you are exposed to them.
32) Suggest three features that you might selectively breed for in a dairy cow.
33) Give two disadvantages of selective breeding.
34) Give three ways that genetic engineering has been used successfully in crop plants.
35) What are the advantages and disadvantages of the cloning technique used in embryo transplants?
36) Three sheep were used to produce Dolly. One provided the egg cell she grew from, another
    provided the nucleus for this cell, and the last gave birth to her. Which sheep was Dolly a clone of?
37) Give three potential benefits and three potential risks of continuing to clone mammals.
38) In plants, where should you take the tissue from to get the best results from a tissue culture?

Leaf Structure

Carbon dioxide + water → glucose + oxygen. Remember that? Well, here's some more...

Leaves are Designed for Making Food by Photosynthesis

The whole structure of leaves is geared towards that.
You need to know all the different parts of a
typical leaf shown on the diagram:

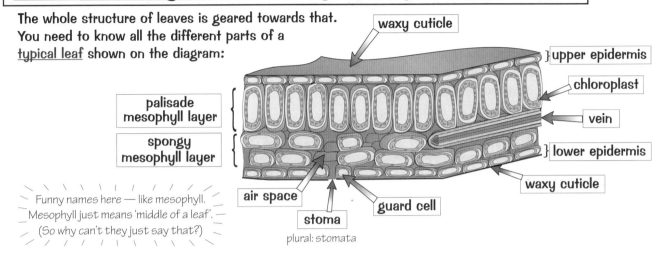

Funny names here — like mesophyll.
Mesophyll just means 'middle of a leaf'.
(So why can't they just say that?)

Labels: waxy cuticle, upper epidermis, chloroplast, vein, lower epidermis, waxy cuticle, palisade mesophyll layer, spongy mesophyll layer, air space, stoma (plural: stomata), guard cell

Learn These Important Features of Leaves

Leaves are adapted for efficient photosynthesis:

1) Leaves are broad, so there's a large surface area exposed to light.

2) They're also thin, which means carbon dioxide and water vapour only have to travel a short distance to reach the photosynthesising cells where it's needed.

3) There are air spaces in the spongy mesophyll layer. This allows gases like carbon dioxide (CO_2) and oxygen (O_2) to move easily between cells. This also means there's a large surface area for gas exchange — the technical phrase for this is "they have a very big internal surface area to volume ratio".

4) Leaves contain lots of chlorophyll, which is the pigment that absorbs light energy for photosynthesis. Chlorophyll is found in chloroplasts, and most of the chloroplasts are found in the palisade layer. This is so that they're near the top of the leaf where they can get the most light.

5) The upper epidermis is transparent so that light can pass through it to the palisade layer.

6) The lower surface is full of little holes called stomata. They're there to let gases like CO_2 and O_2 in and out. They also allow water to escape — which is known as transpiration (see page 62).

7) Leaves have a network of veins. These deliver water and other nutrients to every part of the leaf and take away the food produced by the leaf. They also help to support the leaf structure.

Leaf Palisade Cells are Designed for Photosynthesis

1) They're packed with chloroplasts for photosynthesis.

2) Their tall shape means a lot of surface area is exposed down the side for absorbing CO_2 from the air in the leaf.

3) Their tall shape also means there's a good chance of light hitting a chloroplast before it reaches the bottom of the cell.

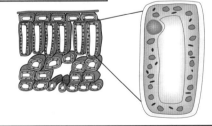

If you don't do much revision, it's time to turn over a new leaf...

So how the heck do they know all this stuff? Well, scientists know how leaves are adapted for photosynthesis because they've looked and seen the structure of leaves and the cells inside them. Not with the naked eye, of course — they used microscopes. So they're not just making it up, after all.

Diffusion in Leaves

You should remember diffusion from module B3 (page 39) — there was loads of it in there.
Don't forget that diffusion is totally <u>random</u> and happens <u>all by itself</u>, so it doesn't use up any energy.

Plants Exchange Gases by Diffusion

When plants photosynthesise they <u>use up CO_2</u> from the atmosphere and <u>produce O_2</u> as a
product. Don't forget that plants also <u>respire</u> (see page 26). During respiration they <u>use up</u>
<u>O_2</u> and <u>produce CO_2</u> as a product. So there are lots of gases moving to and fro in plants,
and this movement happens by <u>diffusion</u>.

Here's the posh way of explaining diffusion again:

> **DIFFUSION is the PASSIVE MOVEMENT OF PARTICLES from an area
> of HIGHER CONCENTRATION to an area of LOWER CONCENTRATION**

Diffusion of <u>Gases in Leaves</u> is Vital for <u>Photosynthesis</u>

This is how diffusion of gases happens in <u>leaves</u> during photosynthesis:

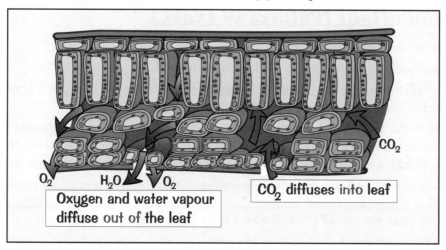

O_2 H_2O O_2

Oxygen and water vapour
diffuse out of the leaf

CO_2 diffuses into leaf

CO_2

When the plant is photosynthesising it uses up lots of <u>CO_2</u>, so there's hardly any inside the leaf.
Luckily this makes <u>more</u> CO_2 move into the leaf by <u>diffusion</u> (from an area of <u>higher</u> concentration to
an area of <u>lower</u> concentration). At the same time lots of <u>O_2</u> is being <u>made</u> as a waste product of
photosynthesis. Some is used in <u>respiration</u>, and the rest diffuses <u>out</u> through the stomata (moving
from an area of <u>higher</u> concentration to an area of <u>lower</u> concentration).

At <u>night</u> it's a different story — there's <u>no photosynthesis</u> going on because there's no <u>light</u>. Lots of
carbon dioxide is made in <u>respiration</u> and lots of oxygen is used up. There's a lot of CO_2 in the leaf and
not a lot of O_2, so now it's mainly carbon dioxide diffusing <u>out</u> and oxygen diffusing <u>in</u>.

<u>Water vapour</u> also escapes from the leaf by diffusion, because there's a lot of it <u>inside</u> the leaf and
less of it in the <u>air outside</u>. This diffusion of water vapour out of leaves is known as <u>transpiration</u>
(see page 62).

Diffusion — silent but deadly...

Particles whizz about so fast that they quickly spread out to cover as much space as possible — that's
why they diffuse. An Austrian scientist called <u>Ludwig Boltzmann</u> developed the theory that gas particles
do this in the <u>1860s</u>. It's quite a tragic story actually — Ludwig was so upset when other scientists
opposed his theory, he killed himself (he was suffering from depression). And he was right all along...

Osmosis

Osmosis is a Special Case of Diffusion, That's All

Osmosis is the movement of water molecules across a partially permeable membrane from a region of higher water concentration to a region of lower water concentration.

1) A partially permeable membrane is just one with very small holes in it. So small, in fact, only tiny molecules (like water) can pass through them, and bigger molecules (e.g. sucrose) can't.

2) The water molecules actually pass both ways through the membrane during osmosis. This happens because water molecules move about randomly all the time.

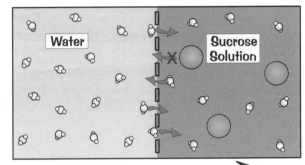

3) But because there are more water molecules on one side than on the other, there's a steady net flow of water into the region with fewer water molecules, i.e. into the stronger glucose solution.

4) This means the strong sugar solution gets more dilute. The water acts like it's trying to 'even up' the concentration either side of the membrane.

Net movement of water molecules

5) Osmosis is a type of diffusion — passive movement of water particles from an area of high water concentration to an area of low water concentration.

Turgor Pressure Supports Plant Tissues

Normal Cell   Turgid Cell

1) When a plant is well watered, all its cells will draw water in by osmosis and become plump and swollen. When the cells are like this, they're said to be turgid.

2) The contents of the cell push against the cell wall — this is called turgor pressure. Turgor pressure helps support the plant tissues.

3) If there's no water in the soil, a plant starts to wilt (droop). This is because the cells start to lose water and so lose their turgor pressure. The cells are then said to be flaccid.

4) If the plant's really short of water, the cytoplasm inside its cells starts to shrink and the membrane pulls away from the cell wall. The cell is now said to be plasmolysed. The plant doesn't totally lose its shape though, because the inelastic cell wall keeps things in position. It just droops a bit.

Flaccid Cell   Plasmolysed Cell

Animal Cells Don't Have an Inelastic Cell Wall

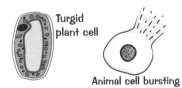

Turgid plant cell

Animal cell bursting

Plant cells aren't too bothered by changes in the amount of water because the inelastic cell wall keeps everything in place.

It's different in animal cells because they don't have a cell wall. If an animal cell takes in too much water, it bursts — this is known as lysis. If it loses too much water it gets all shrivelled up — this is known as crenation.

What all this means is that animals have to keep the amount of water in their cells pretty constant or they're in trouble, while plants are a bit more tolerant of periods of drought.

Revision by osmosis — you wish...

Wouldn't that be great — if all the ideas in this book would just gradually drift across into your mind, from an area of higher concentration (in the book) to an area of lower concentration (in your mind — no offence). Actually, that probably will happen if you read it again. Why don't you give it a go...

Water Flow Through Plants

If you don't water a house plant for a few days it starts to go <u>all droopy</u>. Then it <u>dies</u>, and the people from the Society for the Protection of Plants come round and have you <u>arrested</u>. Plants need water.

Root Hairs Take in Water by Osmosis

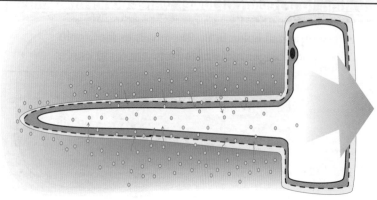

1) The cells on plant roots grow into long '<u>hairs</u>' which stick out into the soil.

2) Each branch of a root will be covered in <u>millions</u> of these microscopic hairs.

3) This gives the plant a <u>big surface area</u> for absorbing <u>water</u> from the soil.

4) There's usually a <u>higher concentration</u> of water in the soil than there is inside the plant, so the water is drawn into the root hair cell by <u>osmosis</u>.

Transpiration is the Loss of Water from the Plant

1) Transpiration is caused by the <u>evaporation</u> and <u>diffusion</u> (see page 60) of water from inside the leaves.

2) This creates a slight <u>shortage</u> of water in the leaf, and so more water is drawn up from the rest of the plant through the <u>xylem vessels</u> (see page 64) to replace it.

3) This in turn means more water is drawn up from the <u>roots</u>, and so there's a constant <u>transpiration stream</u> of water through the plant.

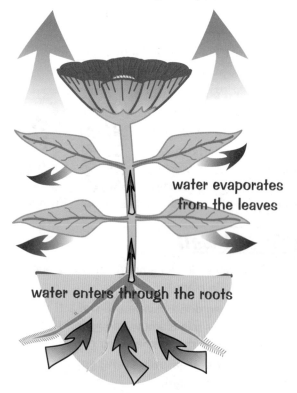

water evaporates from the leaves

water enters through the roots

Transpiration is just a <u>side-effect</u> of the way leaves are adapted for <u>photosynthesis</u>. They have to have <u>stomata</u> in them so that gases can be exchanged easily (see page 63). Because there's more water <u>inside</u> the plant than in the <u>air outside</u>, the water escapes from the leaves through the stomata.

The transpiration stream does have some <u>benefits</u> for the plants, however:

1) The constant stream of water from the ground helps to keep the plant <u>cool</u>.

2) It provides the plant with a constant supply of water for <u>photosynthesis</u>.

3) The water creates <u>turgor pressure</u> in the plant cells, which helps support the plant and stops it wilting (see page 61).

4) <u>Minerals</u> needed by the plant (see page 65) can be brought in from the soil along with the water.

Transpiration — the plant version of perspiration...

Here's an interesting fact — a biggish tree loses about a <u>thousand litres</u> of water from its leaves <u>every single day</u>. That's as much water as the average person drinks in a whole year, so the <u>roots</u> have to be very effective at drawing in water from the soil. Which is why they have all those root <u>hairs</u>, you see.

Water Flow Through Plants

Transpiration Rate is Affected by Four Main Things

1) <u>LIGHT INTENSITY</u> — the <u>brighter</u> the light, the <u>greater</u> the transpiration rate.

<u>Stomata</u> begin to <u>close</u> as it gets darker. Photosynthesis can't happen in the dark, so they don't need to be open to let <u>CO_2</u> in. When the stomata are closed, water can't escape.

2) <u>TEMPERATURE</u> — the <u>warmer</u> it is, the <u>faster</u> transpiration happens.

When it's warm the water particles have <u>more energy</u> to evaporate and diffuse out of the stomata.

3) <u>AIR MOVEMENT</u> — if there's <u>lots</u> of air movement (wind) around a leaf, transpiration happens <u>faster</u>.

If the air around a leaf is very still, the water vapour just <u>surrounds the leaf</u> and doesn't move away. This means there's a <u>high concentration</u> of water particles outside the leaf as well as inside it, so <u>diffusion</u> doesn't happen as quickly. If it's windy, the water vapour is <u>swept away</u>, maintaining a <u>low concentration</u> of water in the air outside the leaf. Diffusion then happens quickly, from an area of high concentration to an area of low concentration.

4) <u>AIR HUMIDITY</u> — if the air around the leaf is very <u>dry</u>, transpiration happens more <u>quickly</u>.

This is like what happens with air movement. If the air is <u>humid</u> there's a lot of water in it already, so there's not much of a <u>difference</u> between the inside and the outside of the leaf. Diffusion happens <u>fastest</u> if there's a <u>really high concentration</u> in one place, and a <u>really low concentration</u> in the other.

Plants Need to Balance Water Loss with Water Uptake

Transpiration can help plants in some ways (see last page), but if it hasn't rained for a while and you're <u>short of water</u> it's not a good idea to have it rushing out of your leaves. So plants have <u>adaptations</u> to help <u>reduce water loss</u> from their leaves.

1) Leaves usually have a <u>waxy cuticle</u> covering the <u>upper epidermis</u>. This helps make the upper surface of the leaf <u>waterproof</u>.

2) Most <u>stomata</u> are found on the <u>lower surface</u> of a leaf where it's <u>darker</u> and <u>cooler</u>. This helps slow down <u>diffusion</u> of water out of the leaf (see above).

3) The <u>bigger</u> the stomata and the <u>more</u> stomata a leaf has, the more <u>water</u> the plant will <u>lose</u>. Plants in <u>hot climates</u> really need to conserve water, so they have <u>fewer</u> and <u>smaller</u> stomata on the underside of the leaf and <u>no</u> stomata on the upper epidermis.

Stomata Open and Close Automatically

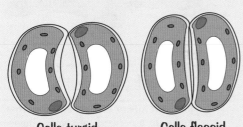

Cells turgid,
stoma opens

Cells flaccid,
stoma closes

1) <u>Stomata</u> close <u>automatically</u> when supplies of water from the roots start to <u>dry up</u>.

2) The <u>guard cells</u> have a special kidney shape which opens and closes the <u>stomata</u> as the guard cells go <u>turgid</u> or <u>flaccid</u>.

3) <u>Thin</u> outer walls and <u>thickened</u> inner walls make this opening and closing function work properly.

4) Open stomata allow gases in and out for <u>photosynthesis</u>.

5) They're sensitive to light and <u>close</u> at <u>night</u> to conserve water without losing out on photosynthesis.

It always helps if you're quick on the uptake...

One good way to remember those <u>four factors</u> that affect the rate of transpiration is to think about drying washing. Then you'll realise there are far more boring things you could be doing than revision, and you'll try harder. No, only joking — it's the same stuff: <u>sunny</u>, <u>warm</u>, <u>windy</u> and <u>dry</u>.

Transport Systems in Plants

Where humans only have <u>one</u> circulatory system, plants have <u>two</u>.
They have <u>two</u> separate types of vessel — <u>xylem</u> and <u>phloem</u> — for transporting stuff around.
<u>Both</u> types of vessel go to <u>every part</u> of the plant, but they are totally <u>separate</u>.

Phloem Tubes Transport Food:

1) Made of columns of living cells with <u>perforated end-plates</u> to allow stuff to flow through.

2) They transport <u>food substances</u> (mainly <u>sugars</u>) made in the leaves to growing and storage tissues, in <u>both directions</u>.

3) This movement of food substances around the plant is known as <u>translocation</u>.

Xylem Tubes Take Water UP:

1) Made of <u>dead cells</u> joined end to end with <u>no</u> end walls between them and a hole (<u>lumen</u>) down the middle.

2) The thick side walls are strong and stiff, which gives the plant <u>support</u>.

3) They carry <u>water</u> and <u>minerals</u> from the <u>roots</u> up the shoot to the leaves in the <u>transpiration stream</u>.

You can Recognise Xylem and Phloem by Where They Are

1) They usually run <u>alongside</u> each other in <u>vascular bundles</u> (like veins).

2) <u>Where</u> they're found in each type of plant structure is related to <u>xylem</u>'s other function — <u>support</u>. You need to learn these <u>three examples</u>:

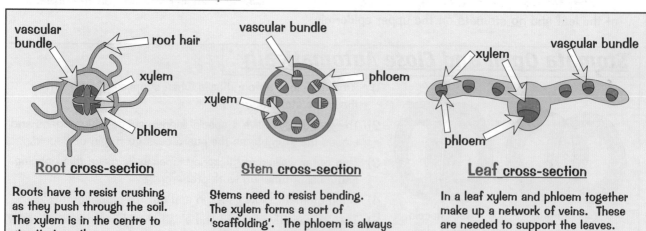

Root cross-section

Roots have to resist crushing as they push through the soil. The xylem is in the centre to give it strength.

Stem cross-section

Stems need to resist bending. The xylem forms a sort of 'scaffolding'. The phloem is always around the outside of the stem.

Leaf cross-section

In a leaf xylem and phloem together make up a network of veins. These are needed to support the leaves.

Don't let revision stress you out — just go with the phloem...

You probably did that really dull experiment at school where you stick a piece of <u>celery</u> in a beaker of water with red food colouring in it. Then you stare at it for half an hour, and once the time is up, hey presto, the red has reached the top of the celery. That's because it travelled there in the <u>xylem</u>.

Minerals Needed for Healthy Growth

Plants are important in <u>food chains</u> and <u>nutrient cycles</u> because they can take <u>minerals</u> from the soil and <u>energy</u> from the Sun and turn it into food. And then, after all that hard work, we eat them.

Plants Need Three Main Minerals

Plants need certain <u>elements</u> so they can produce important compounds. They get these elements from <u>minerals</u> in the <u>soil</u>. If there aren't enough of these minerals in the soil, plants suffer <u>deficiency symptoms</u>.

1) Nitrates

Contain nitrogen for making <u>amino acids</u> and <u>proteins</u>. These are needed for <u>cell growth</u>. If a plant can't get enough nitrates it will be <u>stunted</u> and will have <u>yellow older leaves</u>.

2) Phosphates

Contain phosphorus for making <u>DNA</u> and <u>cell membranes</u> and they're needed for <u>respiration</u> and <u>growth</u>. Plants without enough phosphate have <u>poor root growth</u> and <u>purple older leaves</u>.

3) Potassium

To help the <u>enzymes</u> needed for <u>photosynthesis</u> and <u>respiration</u>. If there's not enough potassium in the soil, plants have <u>poor flower and fruit growth</u> and <u>discoloured leaves</u>.

Magnesium is Also Needed in Small Amounts

The three main minerals are needed in fairly <u>large amounts</u>, but there are other elements which are needed in much <u>smaller</u> amounts. <u>Magnesium</u> is one of the most significant as it's required for making <u>chlorophyll</u> (needed for <u>photosynthesis</u>). Plants without enough magnesium have <u>yellow leaves</u>.

Root Hairs Take In Minerals Using Active Transport

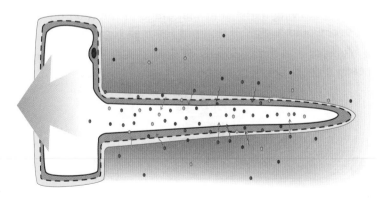

1) <u>Root hairs</u> (see page 62) give the plant a <u>big surface area</u> for absorbing minerals from the soil.

2) But the <u>concentration</u> of minerals in the <u>soil</u> is usually pretty <u>low</u>. It's normally <u>higher</u> in the <u>root hair cell</u> than in the soil around it.

3) So normal diffusion <u>doesn't</u> explain how minerals are taken up into the root hair cell.

4) They should go <u>the other way</u> if they followed the rules of diffusion.

5) The answer is that a different process called '<u>active transport</u>' is responsible.

6) Active transport uses <u>energy</u> from <u>respiration</u> to help the plant pull minerals into the root hair <u>against the concentration gradient</u>. This is essential for its growth.

Nitrogen and phosphorus and potassium — oh my...

When a farmer or a gardener buys <u>fertiliser</u>, that's pretty much what he or she is buying — <u>nitrates</u>, <u>phosphates</u> and <u>potassium</u>. A fertiliser's <u>NPK label</u> tells you the relative proportions of nitrogen (N), phosphorus (P) and potassium (K) it contains, so you can choose the right one for your plants and soil.

Pyramids of Number and Biomass

A <u>trophic level</u> is a <u>feeding</u> level. It comes from the Greek word <u>trophe</u> meaning 'nourishment'. The amount of <u>energy</u>, <u>biomass</u> and usually the <u>number of organisms</u> all <u>decrease</u> as you move up a trophic level.

You Need to be Able to Construct Pyramids of Number

Luckily it's pretty easy — they'll give you all the information you need to do it in the exam. Here's an example:

<u>5000</u> dandelions... feed... <u>100</u> rabbits... which feed... <u>1</u> fox.

1) Each bar on a pyramid of numbers shows the <u>number of organisms</u> at that stage of the food chain.

2) So the '<u>dandelions</u>' bar on this pyramid would need to be <u>longer</u> than the '<u>rabbits</u>' bar, which in turn should be <u>longer</u> than the '<u>fox</u>' bar.

3) <u>Dandelions</u> go at the <u>bottom</u> because they're at the bottom of the food chain.

This gives a <u>typical pyramid of numbers</u>, where every time you go up a <u>trophic (feeding) level</u>, the number of organisms goes <u>down</u>. This is because it takes a <u>lot</u> of food from the level below to keep one animal alive.

| 1 fox |
| 100 rabbits |
| 5000 dandelions |

But there are cases where a number pyramid is <u>not a pyramid at all</u>, like these ones:

| 500 Fleas |
| 1 Fox |
| 100 Rabbits |
| 5000 Dandelions |

| 1 Partridge |
| 500 Ladybirds |
| 3000 Aphids |
| 1 Pear tree |

You'll Have to Construct Pyramids of Biomass Too

1) Each bar on a <u>pyramid of biomass</u> shows the <u>mass of living material</u> at that stage of the food chain — basically how much all the organisms at each level would '<u>weigh</u>' if you put them <u>all together</u>.

2) So the one pear tree above would have a <u>big biomass</u> and the <u>hundreds of fleas</u> would have a <u>very small biomass</u>. Biomass pyramids are practically <u>always the right shape</u>:

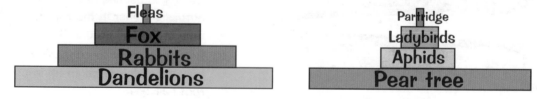

Even if you know nothing about the natural world, you're probably aware that a <u>tree</u> is quite a bit <u>bigger</u> than an <u>aphid</u>. So what's going on here is that <u>lots</u> (probably thousands) of aphids are feeding on a <u>few</u> great big trees. Quite a lot of <u>ladybirds</u> are then eating the aphids, and a few <u>partridges</u> are eating the ladybirds. <u>Biomass</u> and <u>energy</u> are still <u>decreasing</u> as you go up the levels — it's just that <u>one tree</u> can have a very <u>big biomass</u>, and can fix a lot of the <u>Sun's energy</u> using all those leaves.

Constructing pyramids is a breeze — just ask the Egyptians...

There are actually a couple of exceptions where pyramids of <u>biomass</u> aren't quite pyramid-shaped. It happens when the producer has a very short life but reproduces loads, like with plankton at certain times of year. But it's <u>rare</u>, and you <u>don't</u> need to know about it. Forget I ever mentioned it. Sorry.

Energy Transfer and Energy Flow

All That Energy Just Disappears Somehow...

1) Energy from the Sun is the source of energy for nearly all life on Earth.

2) Plants use a small percentage of the light energy from the Sun to make food during photosynthesis. This energy then works its way through the food web as animals eat the plants and each other.

3) The energy lost at each stage is used for staying alive, i.e. in respiration (see pages 2 and 26), which powers all life processes.

4) Most of this energy is eventually lost to the surroundings as heat. This is especially true for mammals and birds, whose bodies must be kept at a constant temperature which is normally higher than their surroundings.

Material and energy are both lost at each stage of the food chain.

HEAT LOSS

MATERIALS LOST IN ANIMAL'S WASTE

5) Material and energy are also lost from the food chain in the droppings — you'll need to remember the posh word for producing droppings, which is egestion.

This explains why you get biomass pyramids. Most of the biomass is lost and so does not become biomass in the next level up.

(There's more about the energy stored in biomass on page 66.)

It also explains why you hardly ever get food chains with more than about five trophic levels. So much energy is lost at each stage that there's not enough left to support more organisms after four or five stages.

You Need to be Able to Interpret Data on Energy Flow

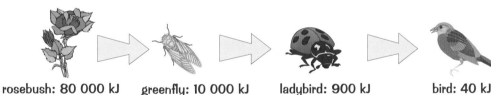

rosebush: 80 000 kJ   greenfly: 10 000 kJ   ladybird: 900 kJ   bird: 40 kJ

1) The numbers show the amount of energy available to the next level. So 80 000 kJ is the amount of energy available to the greenfly, and 10 000 kJ is the amount available to the ladybird.

2) You can work out how much energy has been lost at each level by taking away the energy that is available to the next level from the energy that was available from the previous level. Like this:

Energy lost at 1st trophic level as heat and in egestion = 80 000 kJ – 10 000 kJ = 70 000 kJ lost.

3) You can also calculate the efficiency of energy transfer — this just means how good it is at passing on energy from one level to the next.

$$\text{efficiency} = \frac{\text{energy available to the next level}}{\text{energy that was available to the previous level}} \times 100$$

So at the 1st trophic level, efficiency of energy transfer = 10 000 kJ ÷ 80 000 kJ × 100
= 12.5% efficient.

So when revising, put the fire on and don't take toilet breaks...

No, I'm being silly — go if you have to. We're talking in general terms about whole food chains here — you won't lose your concentration as a direct result of, erm, egestion.

Biomass and Intensive Farming

Energy Stored in Biomass Can be Used for Other Things

There are many different ways to <u>release</u> the <u>energy</u> stored in <u>biomass</u> — including <u>eating it</u>, <u>feeding it to livestock</u>, <u>growing the seeds</u> of plants and <u>using it as a fuel</u>.

<u>For a given area of land</u>, you can produce <u>a lot more food</u> for humans by growing <u>crops</u> than by grazing <u>animals</u> — only about <u>10%</u> of the biomass eaten by beef cattle becomes useful meat for people to eat. It's important to get a <u>balanced diet</u>, though, which is difficult from crops only. It's also worth remembering that <u>some land</u>, like <u>moorland</u> or <u>fellsides</u>, isn't suitable for growing crops. In these places, animals like <u>sheep</u> and <u>deer</u> can be the <u>best way</u> to get food from the land.

As well as using biomass as food, you can use it as fuel. Learn these two examples of <u>biofuels</u>:

1) <u>Fast-growing trees</u> — people tend to think burning trees is a <u>bad thing</u>, but it's not as long as they're <u>fast-growing</u> and planted <u>especially</u> for that purpose. Each time trees are cut down, more can be planted to <u>replace them</u>. There's <u>no</u> overall contribution to CO_2 <u>emissions</u> because the <u>replacement trees</u> are still <u>removing carbon</u> from the atmosphere.

2) <u>Fermenting biomass</u> using <u>bacteria</u> or <u>yeast</u> — fermenting means <u>breaking down</u> by <u>anaerobic respiration</u>. You can use micro-organisms to make <u>biogas</u> from plant and animal <u>waste</u> in a simple fermenter called a <u>digester</u>. The biogas can then be <u>burned</u> to release the energy for <u>heating</u>, powering a <u>turbine</u>, etc.

Developing biofuels is a <u>great</u> idea, for these three important reasons:

* Unlike coal, oil and the like, biofuels are <u>renewable</u> — they're <u>not</u> going to run out one day.
* Using biofuels reduces <u>air pollution</u> — no <u>acid rain gases</u> are produced when wood and biogas burn.
* You can be <u>energy self-reliant</u>. Theoretically, you could supply <u>all</u> your energy from <u>household waste</u>.

Intensive Farming is Used to Produce More Food

<u>Intensive farming</u> means trying to produce <u>as much food as possible</u> from your land, animals and plants. Farmers can do this in different ways, but they all involve <u>reducing</u> the <u>energy losses</u> that happen at each stage in a food chain (see last page). Here are some examples of how they do it:

1) They use <u>herbicides</u> to kill <u>weeds</u>. This means that <u>more</u> of the energy from the Sun falling on their fields goes to the <u>crops</u>, and <u>not</u> to any other <u>competing plants</u> that they don't want.

2) They use <u>pesticides</u> to kill <u>insects</u> that eat the crops. This makes sure no energy is <u>transferred</u> into a <u>different food chain</u> — it's all saved for growing the crops.

3) Animals are <u>battery farmed</u>. They're kept close together indoors in small pens, so that they're warm and can't move about. This saves them <u>wasting energy</u> as they move around, and stops them using up so much energy <u>keeping warm</u>.

<u>Intensive farming</u> allows us to produce <u>a lot of food</u> from <u>less and less land</u>, which means a <u>huge variety</u> of <u>top quality</u> foods, <u>all year round</u>, at <u>cheap prices</u>.

Intensive Farming Can Destroy the Environment

Intensive farming methods are <u>efficient</u>, but they raise <u>ethical dilemmas</u> because they can damage the world we live in, making it <u>polluted</u>, <u>unattractive</u> and <u>devoid of wildlife</u>. The main effects are:

1) <u>Removal of hedges</u> to make huge great fields for <u>maximum efficiency</u>. This <u>destroys the natural habitat</u> of <u>wild creatures</u> and can lead to serious <u>soil erosion</u>.

2) Careless use of <u>fertilisers</u> pollutes <u>rivers</u> and <u>lakes</u> (known as <u>eutrophication</u>).

3) <u>Pesticides disturb food chains</u> — see next page.

4) Lots of people think that intensive farming of <u>animals</u> such as <u>battery-hens</u> is <u>cruel</u>.

Be energy self-reliant — burn poo...

One of the saddest things about intensive farming methods is that it reduces the <u>wildlife</u> in the countryside. If there are <u>no plants</u> (except crops) and <u>few insects</u>, there's not much around to eat...

Pesticides and Biological Control

Biological control is growing <u>more popular</u>, as people get fed up with all the problems caused by <u>pesticides</u>.

Pesticides Disturb Food Chains

1) <u>Pesticides</u> are sprayed onto crops to kill the creatures that <u>damage</u> them, but unfortunately they also kill lots of <u>harmless</u> animals such as bees and beetles.

2) This can cause a <u>shortage of food</u> for animals further up the food chain.

3) Pesticides also tend to be <u>toxic</u> to creatures that aren't pests and there's a danger of the poison <u>passing on</u> through the food chain to other animals. There's even a risk that they could harm <u>humans</u>.

This is well illustrated by the case of <u>otters</u> which were almost <u>wiped out</u> over much of crop-dominated southern England by a pesticide called <u>DDT</u> in the early 1960s. The diagram shows the <u>food chain</u> which ends with the <u>otter</u>. DDT can't be <u>excreted</u>, so it <u>accumulates</u> along the <u>food chain</u> and the <u>otter</u> ends up with <u>most</u> of the <u>DDT</u> collected by all the other animals.

③ Each little tiny animal eats lots of small plants

⑤ Each eel eats lots of small fish

① Insecticide seeps into the river

② Small water plants take up a little insecticide

④ Each small fish eats lots of tiny animals

⑥ Each otter eats lots of eels

You Can Use Biological Control Instead of Pesticides

<u>Biological control</u> means using <u>living things</u> instead of chemicals to control a pest.
You could use a <u>predator</u>, a <u>parasite</u> or a <u>disease</u> to kill the pest. For example:

1) <u>Aphids</u> are a pest because they eat <u>roses</u> and <u>vegetables</u>. <u>Ladybirds</u> are aphid <u>predators</u>, so people release them into their fields and gardens to keep aphid numbers down.

2) Certain types of <u>wasps</u> and <u>flies</u> produce <u>larvae</u> which develop on (or in, yuck) a <u>host insect</u>. This eventually <u>kills</u> the insect host. Lots of insect pests have <u>parasites</u> like this.

3) <u>Myxomatosis</u> is a <u>disease</u> which kills <u>rabbits</u>. The <u>myxoma virus</u> was released in <u>Australia</u> as a biological control when the rabbit population there grew out of control and ruined crops.

You need to be able to explain the <u>advantages</u> and <u>disadvantages</u> of <u>biological control</u>:

<u>ADVANTAGES</u>:

* The predator, parasite or disease usually <u>only affects the pest animal</u>. You don't kill all the harmless and helpful creatures as well like you often do with a pesticide.
* No chemicals are used, so there's less <u>pollution</u>, disruption of <u>food chains</u> and risk to <u>people</u> eating the food that's been sprayed.

<u>DISADVANTAGES</u>:

* It's <u>slower</u> than pesticides — you have to wait for your control organism to build up its numbers.
* Biological control won't kill <u>all</u> the pests, and it usually only kills <u>one type</u> of pest.
* It takes more <u>management</u> and <u>planning</u>, and workers might need <u>training</u> or <u>educating</u>.
* Control organisms can <u>drive out</u> native species, or become <u>pests</u> in their own right.

Remember that <u>removing</u> an organism from a food web, whether you use <u>biological control</u> or <u>pesticides</u>, can affect <u>all</u> the other organisms too. For example, if you remove a pest insect, you're removing a source of <u>food</u> from all the organisms that normally eat it. These might <u>die out</u>, and another insect that they normally feed on could <u>breed out of control</u> and become a pest instead. You have to be very careful.

Don't get bugged by biological pest control...

In the exam you might be asked to <u>interpret data</u> related to biological control, e.g. tables showing the population sizes of pest species when using biological control and when using pesticides. Or they might give you a food web and ask you to <u>predict the effect</u> of removing different organisms.

Alternatives to Intensive Farming

Intensive farming methods are <u>still used</u>, a lot. But people are also using <u>other</u> methods more and more.

Hydroponics is Where Plants are Grown Without Soil

Most commercially grown <u>tomatoes</u> and <u>cucumbers</u> are grown in <u>nutrient solutions</u> (water and fertilisers) instead of in soil — this is called <u>hydroponics</u>.

There are <u>advantages</u> and <u>disadvantages</u> of using hydroponics instead of growing crops in soil:

ADVANTAGES	DISADVANTAGES
Takes up less space so less land required	It can be expensive to set up and run
No soil preparation or weeding needed	Need to use specially formulated soluble nutrients
Can still grow plants even in areas with poor soil	Growers need to be skilled and properly trained
Many pest species live in soil, so it avoids these	There's no soil to anchor the roots so plants need support
Mineral levels can be controlled more accurately	

Organic Farming is Still Perfectly Viable

Modern intensive farming produces lots of <u>food</u> and we all appreciate it on the supermarket shelves. But traditional <u>organic farming</u> methods do still work (amazingly!), and they have their <u>benefits</u> too. You need to know about these organic farming <u>techniques</u>:

1) Use of <u>organic fertilisers</u> (i.e. animal manure and compost). This <u>recycles</u> the nutrients left in plant and animal waste. It <u>doesn't work as well</u> as artificial fertilisers, but it is better for the <u>environment</u>.

2) <u>Crop rotation</u> — growing a cycle of <u>different crops</u> in a field each year. This stops the <u>pests</u> and <u>diseases</u> of one crop building up, and stops <u>nutrients</u> running out (as each crop has slightly <u>different needs</u>). Most crop rotations include a <u>legume plant</u> like peas or beans, as they help put <u>nitrates</u> back in the soil (see page 73).

3) <u>Weeding</u> — this means <u>physically removing</u> the weeds, rather than just spraying them with a <u>herbicide</u>. Obviously it's a lot more <u>labour intensive</u>, but there are no nasty <u>chemicals</u> involved.

4) <u>Varying seed planting times</u> — sowing seeds later or earlier in the season will <u>avoid</u> the <u>major pests</u> for that crop. This means the farmer <u>won't</u> need to use <u>pesticides</u>.

5) <u>Biological control</u> — this is covered on the previous page.

You also need to be able to discuss the <u>advantages</u> and <u>disadvantages</u> of organic farming. Always try to give a <u>balanced</u> point of view, unless you're specifically asked to argue one way or another. You can include your <u>own opinion</u> in a conclusion at the end. Here are a few points you could mention:

1) Organic farming takes up <u>more space</u> than intensive farming — so more land has to be <u>farmland</u>, rather than being set aside for wildlife or for other uses.

2) It's more <u>labour-intensive</u>. This provides <u>more jobs</u>, but it also makes the food more <u>expensive</u>.

3) You can't grow <u>as much</u> food. But on the other hand, Europe <u>over-produces</u> food these days anyway.

4) Organic farming uses fewer <u>chemicals</u>, so there's less risk of toxic chemicals remaining on food.

5) It's better for the <u>environment</u>. There's less chance of <u>polluting rivers</u> with fertiliser. Organic farmers also avoid using <u>pesticides</u>, so don't disrupt food chains and harm wildlife.

6) For a farm to be classed as organic, it will usually have to follow guidelines on the <u>ethical treatment of animals</u>. This means <u>no</u> battery farming.

Plants without soil? It's not like when I was a lad...

You can't just learn about the <u>methods</u> used in different types of farming — you have to think about their <u>impact</u> too. That means weighing up the advantages and disadvantages and being able to discuss them.

Decay

Micro-organisms are great because they break down plant and animal remains which are lying around and looking unsightly. But they also break down plant and animal remains that we just bought at the shops.

Things Decay Because of Micro-organisms

1) Living things are made of materials they take from the world around them.

2) When they die and decompose, or release material as waste, the elements they contain are returned to the soil or air where they originally came from.

3) These elements are then used by plants to grow and the whole cycle repeats over and over again.

4) Nearly all the decomposition is done by soil bacteria and fungi (see next page).

5) This happens everywhere in nature, and also in compost heaps and sewage works.

6) All the important elements are thus recycled, including carbon, hydrogen, oxygen and nitrogen.

7) The rate of decay depends on three main things:

a) Temperature — a warm temperature makes things decay faster because it speeds up respiration in decomposers.

b) Moisture — things decay faster when they're moist because decomposers need water.

c) Oxygen (air) — decay is faster when there's oxygen available. The decomposers can respire aerobically, providing more energy.

8) These factors cause decomposers (bacteria and fungi) to grow and reproduce more quickly, so there'll be more of them to decay other living things.

An energetic decomposer

Food Preservation Methods Reduce the Rate of Decay

Decomposers are good for returning nutrients to the soil, but they're not so good when they start decomposing your lunch. So people have come up with ways to stop them:

1) Canning — basically, this involves putting food in an airtight can. This keeps the decomposers out. After canning, the tin and its contents are heated to a high temperature to kill any micro-organisms that might have been lurking in there already.

2) Cooling — the easiest way to keep food cool is put it in a fridge. Cooling slows down decay because it slows down respiration in the micro-organisms. They can't reproduce as fast either.

3) Freezing — food lasts longer in the freezer than in the fridge because the micro-organisms can't respire or reproduce at all at such low temperatures. Some (but not all) are killed when the water inside them expands as it freezes.

4) Drying — dried food lasts longer because micro-organisms need water. Lots of fruits are preserved by drying them out, and sometimes meat is too.

5) Adding salt — if there's a high concentration of salt around decomposers, they'll lose water by osmosis. This damages them and means they can't work properly. Things like tuna and olives are often stored in brine (salt water).

6) Adding vinegar — mmm, pickled onions. Vinegar is acidic, and the low pH inhibits the enzymes inside the micro-organisms. This stops them decomposing the delicious onions.

Decomposers — they're just misunderstood...

OK, so it's annoying when you go to the cupboard and find that everything has turned a funny green colour. But imagine the alternative — when a plant or animal died, it would just stay there, hanging around. Soon we'd be up to our eyes in dead things, and there'd be no nutrients in the soil. Not good.

72

The Carbon Cycle

Carbon is constantly moving between the atmosphere, the soil and living things in the carbon cycle.

Detritivores and Saprophytes Feed on Decaying Material

Detritivores and saprophytes are both types of organism that are important in decay. They're grouped into those two types depending on how they feed.

1) Detritivores feed on dead and decaying material (detritus). Examples of detritivores include earthworms, maggots and woodlice. As these detritivores feed on the decaying material, they break it up into smaller bits. This gives a bigger surface area for smaller decomposers to work on and so speeds up decay.

2) Saprophytes feed on decaying material by extracellular digestion, i.e. they feed by secreting digestive enzymes on to the material outside of their cells. The enzymes break down the material into smaller bits which can then be absorbed by the saprophyte. Most saprophytes are bacteria and fungi.

The Carbon Cycle Shows How Carbon is Recycled

Carbon is an important element in the materials that living things are made from. It's constantly recycled:

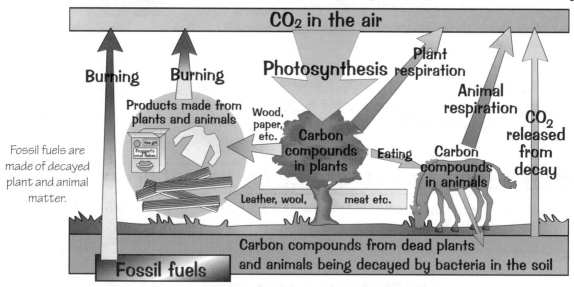

This diagram isn't half as bad as it looks. Learn these important points:

1) There's only one arrow going down. The whole thing is 'powered' by photosynthesis.

2) In photosynthesis plants convert the carbon from CO_2 in the air into sugars. Plants can now incorporate this carbon into carbohydrates, fats and proteins as well.

3) Eating passes the carbon compounds in the plant along to animals in a food chain or web.

4) Both plant and animal respiration while the organisms are alive releases CO_2 back into the air.

5) Plants and animals eventually die and decay, or are killed and turned into useful products.

6) When plants and animals decay they're broken down by bacteria and fungi. These decomposers release CO_2 back into the air by respiration as they break down the material.

7) Some useful plant and animal products, e.g. wood and fossil fuels, are burned (combustion). This also releases CO_2 back into the air.

There's another major recycling pathway for carbon in the sea. Marine organisms make shells made of carbonates. When they die the shells fall to the ocean floor and eventually form limestone rocks. The carbon in these rocks may return to the atmosphere as CO_2 during volcanic eruptions or weathering.

Come on out, it's only a little carbon cycle, it can't hurt you...

Carbon is a very important element for living things — it's the basis for all the organic molecules (fats, proteins, carbohydrates etc.) in our bodies. In sci-fi programmes the aliens are sometimes silicon-based instead, but then they're usually defeated in the end by some Bruce Willis type anyway.

Module B4 — It's a Green World

The Nitrogen Cycle

Nitrogen, just like carbon, is constantly being <u>recycled</u>. So the nitrogen in your proteins might once have been in the <u>air</u>. And before that it might have been in a <u>plant</u>. Or even in some <u>horse wee</u>. Nice.

Nitrogen *is Also Recycled* in the Nitrogen Cycle

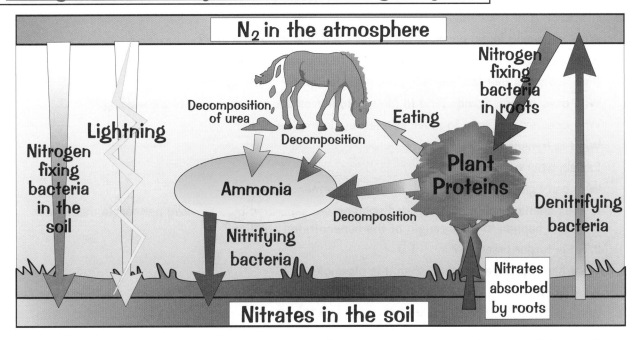

1) The <u>atmosphere</u> contains <u>78% nitrogen gas</u>, N_2. This is <u>very unreactive</u> and so it can't be used <u>directly</u> by plants or animals.

2) <u>Nitrogen</u> is <u>needed</u> for making <u>proteins</u> for growth, so living organisms have to get it somehow.

3) Plants get their nitrogen from the <u>soil</u>, so nitrogen in the air has to be turned into <u>nitrates</u> before plants can use it. <u>Animals</u> can only get <u>proteins</u> by eating plants (or each other).

4) <u>Decomposers</u> break down <u>proteins</u> in rotting plants and animals, and <u>urea</u> in animal waste, into <u>ammonia</u>. So the nitrogen in these organisms is <u>recycled</u>.

5) <u>Nitrogen fixation</u> isn't an obsession with nitrogen — it's the process of turning <u>N_2 from the air</u> into <u>nitrogen compounds</u> in the soil which <u>plants can use</u>. There are <u>two main ways</u> that this happens:
   a) <u>Lightning</u> — there's so much <u>energy</u> in a bolt of lightning that it's enough to make nitrogen <u>react with oxygen</u> in the air to give nitrates.
   b) <u>Nitrogen-fixing bacteria</u> in roots and soil (see below).

6) There are <u>four</u> different types of <u>bacteria</u> involved in the nitrogen cycle:
   a) <u>DECOMPOSERS</u> — decompose <u>proteins</u> and <u>urea</u> and turn them into <u>ammonia</u>.
   b) <u>NITRIFYING BACTERIA</u> — turn <u>ammonia</u> in decaying matter into <u>nitrates</u>.
   c) <u>NITROGEN-FIXING BACTERIA</u> — turn <u>atmospheric N_2</u> into <u>nitrogen compounds</u> that plants can use.
   d) <u>DENITRIFYING BACTERIA</u> — turn <u>nitrates</u> back into <u>N_2 gas</u>. This is of no benefit to living organisms.

7) Some <u>nitrogen-fixing bacteria</u> live in the <u>soil</u>. Others live in <u>nodules</u> on the roots of <u>legume plants</u>. This is why legume plants are so good at putting nitrogen <u>back into the soil</u> (see page 70). The plants have a <u>mutualistic relationship</u> with the bacteria — the bacteria get <u>food</u> (sugars) from the plant, and the plant gets <u>nitrogen compounds</u> from the bacteria to make into <u>proteins</u>. So the relationship benefits both of them.

It's the cyyyycle of liiiiife...

People sometimes forget that when we breathe in, we're breathing in mainly <u>nitrogen</u>. It's a pretty <u>boring</u> gas, colourless and with no taste or smell. But nitrogen is <u>vital</u> to living things, because the <u>amino acids</u> that join together to make <u>proteins</u> (like enzymes) all contain nitrogen.

Revision Summary for Module B4

What a nice leafy section that was. Things started to get a bit mouldy towards the end, but that's life I suppose. Now, just to make sure you've taken in all the leafiness and mouldiness, here's a little revision summary so you can check what you've learned. You know the routine by now — whizz through the questions and make a note of any you can't answer. Then go back and find the answer in the section. It's actually kind of fun, like a treasure hunt... well, okay, it's not — but it works.

1) What is usually found covering the upper epidermis layer of a leaf?
2) How does being broad and thin help a leaf to photosynthesise?
3) Give two ways that leaf palisade cells are adapted for photosynthesis.
4) Why does carbon dioxide tend to move into leaves when they're photosynthesising?
5) Why does oxygen tend to move into leaves during the night?
6) What is transpiration?
7) Explain what osmosis is.
8) Why can't glucose pass through a partially permeable membrane?
9) A weak solution and a concentrated solution are separated by a partially permeable membrane. What will happen to the strength of the concentrated solution?
10) What is turgor pressure?
11) What has happened to a cell when it is plasmolysed?
12) What is crenation? Why doesn't it happen to plant cells?
13) What is the advantage to a plant of having root hairs?
14) Give three ways that the transpiration stream benefits a plant.
15) How is the transpiration rate affected by: a) increased temperature, b) increased air humidity?
16) What causes stomata to close when a plant is short of water? How does this benefit the plant?
17) Give the term for the transport of sugars around a plant.
18) How are xylem vessels adapted to their function?
19) What is a vascular bundle?
20) Where are the xylem and phloem found in a root?
21) Name the three main minerals plants need for healthy growth.
22) How can you tell by looking at a plant that it isn't getting enough phosphates?
23) What is magnesium needed for in a plant?
24) What is active transport? Why is it used in the roots of a plant?
25) Explain why number pyramids are not always pyramid-shaped.
26) What does each bar on a pyramid of biomass represent?
27) What is the source of all the energy in a typical food chain?
28) Why is it unusual to find a food chain with more than five trophic levels?
29) Give three ways that intensive farming methods reduce the energy lost at each stage in a food chain.
30) Give three problems associated with intensive farming.
31) What is meant by the term hydroponics?
32) What is crop rotation?
33) Give two advantages and two disadvantages of organic farming methods.
34) Why do dead organisms decay faster when it is warm?
35) Why does pickling food in vinegar help it to last for longer without decaying?
36) Give an example of a detritivore.
37) How does carbon enter the carbon cycle from the air?
38) What important role do nitrogen-fixing bacteria play in the nitrogen cycle?

Bones and Cartilage

Bones and joints are pretty darned important — without them you wouldn't be able to move around at all. All you'd do is wobble around on the floor like a big squidgy thing.

If You Didn't Have a Skeleton, You'd be Jelly-like

1) The job of a skeleton is to support the body and allow it to move — as well as protect vital organs.

2) Fish, amphibians, reptiles, birds and mammals are all vertebrates — they all have a backbone and an internal skeleton. Other animals (e.g. insects) have their skeleton on the outside.

3) An internal skeleton has certain advantages
- It can easily grow with the body.
- It's easy to attach muscles to it.
- It's more flexible than an external skeleton.

Bones are Living Tissues...

Bones are a lot cleverer than they might look...

1) Bones are made up of living cells — so they grow, and can repair themselves if they get damaged.

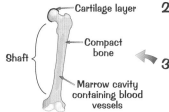

Cartilage layer

Shaft

Compact bone

Marrow cavity containing blood vessels

2) Long bones (e.g. the big one in your thigh) are actually hollow — this makes them lighter than solid bones of the same size (and stronger than solid bones of the same mass). This makes movement far more efficient.

3) The hole in the middle of some long bones is filled with bone marrow. Bone marrow is a spongy substance that makes new blood cells — meaning your bones are actually a kind of blood factory.

...That Start Off Life as Cartilage

1) Bones start off as cartilage in the womb. (Cartilage is living tissue that looks and feels a bit rubbery.)

2) As you grow, cartilage is replaced by bone. Blood vessels deposit calcium and phosphorus in the cartilage — which eventually turns it into bone. This process is called ossification.

3) You can tell if someone is still growing by looking at how much cartilage is present — if there's a lot, they're still growing.

4) Even when you're fully grown, the ends of bones remain covered with cartilage (to stop bones rubbing together at joints — see next page).

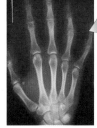

Bones show up on an X-ray, but cartilage doesn't.

X-rays can also show where fractures are.

Bones and Cartilage Can Get Damaged

1) Cartilage and bone are both made up of living tissue, and so can get infected. (The top of the ear is made of cartilage — if you get this pierced, you have to make sure no infection gets in. Not nice.)

2) Even though bones are really strong, they can be fractured (broken) by a sharp knock. Elderly people are more prone to breaking bones as they often suffer from osteoporosis — a condition where calcium is lost from the bones. (Osteoporosis makes the bones softer, more brittle and more likely to break — it can be treated with calcium supplements.)

3) A broken bone can easily injure nearby tissue — so you shouldn't move anyone who might have a fracture. That's especially true for someone with a suspected spinal fracture (broken back) — moving them could damage their spinal cord (basically an extension of the brain running down the middle of the backbone). Damage to the spinal cord can lead to paralysis.

No bones about it... it's a humerus page...

Bones are all too easily thought of as just organic scaffolding. But they're pretty amazing really, and painful if you break one. Talking of broken bones... there are different kinds of break. You've got simple fractures, compound fractures (where the bone pokes through the skin), green-stick fractures... and so on. But bones usually mend pretty easily — if you hold them still, a break will knit itself together.

Joints and Muscles

Like it says in the song, the knee bone's connected to the thigh bone. And it's done with a joint. Read on.

Joints Allow the Bones to Move

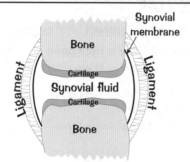

1) The bones at a joint are held together by ligaments. Ligaments have tensile strength (i.e. you can pull them and they don't snap easily) but are pretty elastic (stretchy).

2) The ends of bones are covered with cartilage to stop the bones rubbing together. And because cartilage can be slightly compressed, it can act as a shock absorber.

3) Membranes at joints release oily synovial fluid to lubricate the joints, allowing them to move more easily.

4) Different kinds of joints move in different ways. For example...

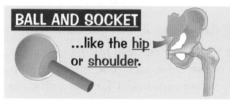

BALL AND SOCKET ...like the hip or shoulder. The joint can move in all directions, and can also rotate.

HINGE ...like the knee or elbow. The joint can go backwards and forwards, but not side-to-side.

Muscles Pull on Bones to Move Them

1) Bones are attached to muscles by tendons.

2) Muscles move bones at a joint by contracting (becoming shorter). They can only pull on bones to move a joint — they can't push.

3) This is why muscles usually come in pairs (called antagonistic pairs). When one muscle in the pair contracts, the joint moves in one direction. When the other contracts, it moves in the opposite direction.

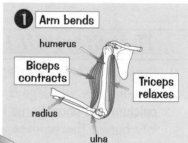

❶ Arm bends — humerus, Biceps contracts, Triceps relaxes, radius, ulna

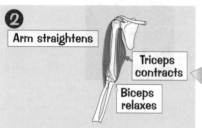

❷ Arm straightens — Triceps contracts, Biceps relaxes

4) The biceps and triceps are an antagonistic pair of muscles. When the biceps contracts it pulls the lower arm upwards. And when the triceps contracts the lower arm is pulled back down.

5) Together, they make the arm work as a lever, where the elbow is the pivot.

Joints Can be Replaced

If your hip or knee joints get damaged or diseased, they can be replaced with artificial joints. Assuming all goes well, you'll be in less pain and discomfort, and able to walk better. But there are disadvantages...

1) The surrounding tissue may become inflamed and painful — this is caused by the body's reaction to the material the joint is made of.

2) Hip dislocation (ball comes out of its socket) is more common with artificial joints, as are blood clots.

3) There's a risk of infection, as with any surgery.

4) The length of the legs may be slightly different, causing difficulty walking.

5) Artificial joints don't last forever — they usually have to be replaced after 12-15 years.

What's a skeleton's favourite instrument?... a trom-bone...

Different joints have different ranges of movement. And if you do something that makes the bone move further than its range of movement (like fall on it), then you could dislocate it. Painful.

The Circulatory System

The circulatory system is everything to do with your <u>heart</u> and your <u>blood</u>. It's the circulatory system that takes food and oxygen round the body, and removes the waste products from your tissues. It's ace.

Humans Have a Double Circulatory System

1) In any circulatory system (so this goes for humans, dogs, fish, etc.), the heart acts as a <u>pump</u>. The heart contracts, <u>pushing</u> blood round the body. Blood flows <u>away</u> from the heart along <u>arteries</u>, through <u>capillaries</u> at the organs, and then back to the heart through <u>veins</u>.

2) As blood travels round the body through blood vessels it <u>loses pressure</u>. So arteries have the <u>highest pressure</u>, veins have the <u>lowest</u> and capillaries are <u>in between</u>.

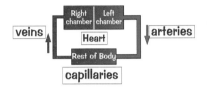

3) Lots of animals (e.g. fish) have a single circulatory system. For this, you need a <u>two-chambered</u> heart.

4) Humans (and loads of other animals) have a <u>double circulatory system</u>. It's kinda like two single circulatory systems stuck together — one circuit goes to the body, the other to the lungs.

5) In a double pump system, you have a <u>four-chambered</u> heart (which you might know already — but if not, see page 44).

6) Different <u>organs</u> need <u>different volumes</u> of blood depending on what they're doing. For example, when you're sitting about, your muscles get about 750 cm³ of blood a minute — but when you <u>exercise</u> they can get over 8 dm³ of blood a minute.

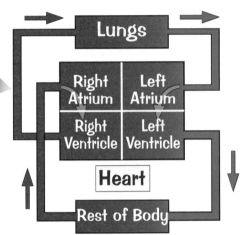

The Cardiac Cycle is How the Heart Contracts

The sequence of events in <u>one complete heartbeat</u> is called the <u>cardiac cycle</u>:

① <u>Blood flows into</u> the two <u>atria</u>.

② The <u>atria contract</u>, pushing the blood into the <u>ventricles</u>.

③ The <u>ventricles contract</u>, forcing the blood into the <u>aorta</u> and the <u>pulmonary artery</u>.

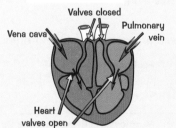 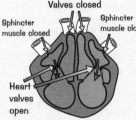 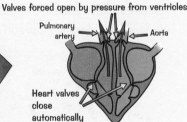

④ The blood then flows along the arteries, the atria fill again and the whole <u>cycle</u> starts over.

We Haven't Always Known This Much About the Heart

<u>Claudius Galen</u> was an <u>ancient Greek</u> doctor. He cut up animals to study them, and so knew about <u>chambers</u> in the heart. He thought <u>arterial</u> blood was <u>made</u> by the heart, while blood in <u>veins</u> was <u>made</u> by the <u>liver</u>, <u>sucked</u> through veins by the heart and <u>consumed</u> by the organs.

<u>William Harvey</u> (1578-1657). Before Harvey, scientists still believed more or less the same as Galen. Harvey changed all this. He showed what the <u>heart valves</u> did, he showed that the heart is a <u>pump</u> (rather than something that <u>sucks</u>), and he showed that the <u>same blood</u> was <u>circulated</u> around the body <u>over and over again</u> — not <u>manufactured</u> and <u>consumed</u>.

Cardiac cycle — why do you miss when my baby kisses me...

If anyone (e.g. an examiner) asks you why their small intestine is suddenly being supplied with <u>more blood</u>, tell them it's probably because they've just had a meal, and their <u>digestive system</u> is <u>busy</u>. Easy.

The Heart

You may have wondered what keeps your heart beating in such regular time. Or you may not have. But it's pretty interesting, so you should keep on reading.

Heart Rate Changes According to Activity

1) When you <u>exercise</u>, your muscles need more oxygen to work harder, so you need to breathe faster. Your <u>heart</u> also <u>pumps faster</u> to deliver more oxygenated blood to your muscles. (And when you stop exercising your heart gradually returns to normal.)

What happens is that your muscles produce more carbon dioxide — this change is detected by the brain, which tells your body to breathe faster.

2) <u>Hormones</u> can also affect your heart rate, e.g. <u>adrenaline</u> is released when you get a shock or you're in danger (it causes the 'fight or flight' response which revs your body up to run away from danger). It <u>increases heart rate</u> to make sure the muscles have plenty of oxygen.

The Heart Has a Pacemaker

1) The heart is told <u>how fast to beat</u> by a group of cells called the <u>pacemaker cells</u>.

2) These cells produce a small <u>electric current</u> which spreads to the surrounding muscle cells, causing them to <u>contract</u>.

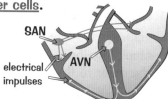

3) There are <u>two</u> clusters of these cells in the heart:
   The <u>sino-atrial node</u> (SAN) stimulates the <u>atria</u> to contract.
   The <u>atrio-ventricular node</u> (AVN) stimulates the <u>ventricles</u> to contract.

4) In one complete heartbeat the SAN produces an electric current <u>first</u>, which spreads to the atria (making them contract). The current stimulates the AVN to produce an electric current (causing the ventricles to contract). This process ensures that the <u>atria always contract before the ventricles</u>.

5) An <u>artificial pacemaker</u> can be used to control heartbeat if the pacemaker cells don't work properly. It's a little device that's implanted under the skin and has a wire going to the heart. It produces an electric current.

ECGs and Echocardiograms Measure the Heart

Doctors can measure how well the heart is working (<u>heart function</u>) in two main ways.

1) <u>Electrocardiogram</u> (ECG) — showing the <u>electrical activity</u> of the heart. They can show:
   • <u>heart attacks</u> — e.g. if you're having a heart attack, or are about to have one,
   • <u>irregular heartbeats</u> and <u>general health</u> of the heart.

This is what a healthy person's ECG looks like...

...and here are some unhealthy ones.

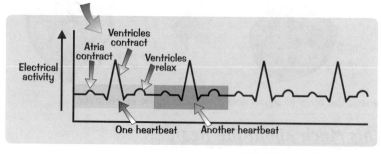

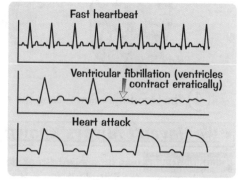

2) <u>Echocardiogram</u> — an <u>ultrasound scan</u> of the heart, which can show: • enlarged heart — this could indicate heart failure,
   • decreased pumping ability — this could indicate a disease called cardiomyopathy,
   • valve function — torn, infected or scarred heart valves can cause problems.

A stitch — the best running pacemaker in the world...

In the exam you might be asked to <u>interpret</u> an ECG — they look scary but they're not too difficult... If a <u>peak</u> is <u>missing</u>, then that part of the heart <u>isn't contracting</u>. If the peaks are <u>close together</u>, the heart's beating <u>faster</u>. But if everything is going <u>haywire</u>, then it could be a <u>heart attack</u> or <u>fibrillation</u>.

Heart Disease

Heart disease is getting more and more common in the developed world.

There are Three Main Ways Your Heart Can Go Wrong

1) Hole in the heart A hole in the heart is usually something you're born with. It's a gap in the wall separating either the two ventricles or the two atria. Oxygen-rich blood on the left-hand side of the heart (that should be sent round the body) instead leaks to the right side and gets sent back to the lungs. This isn't very efficient, and means the heart has to pump extra hard to make up the difference. It can usually be corrected by fairly minor surgery.

2) Valve damage The valves in the heart can be damaged by heart attacks, infection or old age. The damage may cause the valve not to open properly, causing high blood pressure. It may even allow blood to flow in both directions rather than just forward. Severe valve damage is treated by replacing the valve — with an artificial one, or one from a donor or an animal.

3) Coronary heart disease (CHD) Coronary heart disease is when the arteries that supply blood to the muscle of the heart get blocked by fatty deposits. This often results in a heart attack. It can be treated by a coronary bypass operation, where a piece of blood vessel is taken from another part of the body and inserted to 'bypass' the blockage.

Fatty deposits

Vein taken from the leg

You can have surgery to put a lot of heart problems right. For example...

• You can have a heart transplant — an entirely new heart from a donor.

• You can also get new bits fitted, such as valves and pacemakers.

• You can get a heart assist device — this takes over the pumping duties of a failing heart. This 'buys time' while the patient waits for a transplant.

Also have a look at page 45 for some stuff on artificial valves and pacemakers.

Lifestyle Affects the Circulatory System

There are several common lifestyle 'risk factors' for heart disease...

1) Unhealthy diet — eating too much saturated fat can raise the level of cholesterol in the blood. This can clog up your blood vessels and leads to coronary heart disease. Too much salt can raise blood pressure and put an extra strain on your heart.

2) Drinking alcohol — drinking small amounts of alcohol doesn't harm the heart, but regular drinking can raise blood pressure and increase fat levels in the blood.

3) Smoking — smoking can increase your blood pressure, and is a major cause of heart disease.

4) Stress — a small amount of stress is fine, but continual or excessive stress raises blood pressure.

5) Drugs — certain 'recreational' drugs (particularly cocaine, ecstasy and amphetamines) raise your heart rate and blood pressure. The effect is not permanent, but it's dangerous for anyone with heart problems to take these drugs. Cannabis also increases the heart rate, and causes complex changes in blood pressure. Also, cannabis is mostly smoked with tobacco, which doesn't do your heart any good.

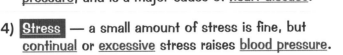

Take care while eating chips — it's a dangerous activity...

In your exam they may ask you to consider the advantages and disadvantages of a heart transplant. Lucky you already know all about them, eh. No... well, you'd better flick back to page 45 then.

Module B5 — The Living Body

Blood

If you get a cut, you don't want all your blood to drain away — this is why <u>clotting</u> is so handy. Sometimes injuries are so bad you lose a lot of blood and you need to replace it — that's where <u>transfusions</u> come in. [The structure of blood cells is covered in Module B3 (page 42) — look at these pages for a more detailed description of red blood cells, white blood cells and plasma.]

Blood Sometimes Doesn't Clot Properly

1) When you're injured, your blood <u>clots</u> to <u>prevent too much</u> <u>bleeding</u>. <u>Platelets</u> clump together to 'plug' the damaged area. In a clot, platelets are held together by a mesh of a protein called <u>fibrin</u> (though this process also needs other proteins called <u>clotting factors</u> to work properly).

<u>PLATELETS</u>
These are small fragments of cells that help blood clot.

2) Some substances in food (and drink) affect the way the blood clots:
   • <u>Vitamin K</u> — this is needed for blood to clot properly. <u>Green vegetables</u> contain lots of vitamin K.
   • <u>Alcohol</u> — a moderate intake of alcohol slows blood clotting.
   • <u>Cranberries</u> — it's been suggested that they may slow blood clotting (but more research is needed).

3) Too little clotting could mean you bleed to death (well, you're more likely to get loads of bruises). Too much clotting can cause <u>strokes</u> and <u>deep vein thrombosis</u> (DVT).

4) People who are at risk of stroke and DVT can take <u>drugs</u> to reduce their risk. <u>Warfarin</u>, <u>heparin</u> and <u>aspirin</u> all help <u>prevent</u> the blood from clotting.

5) <u>Haemophilia</u> is a <u>genetic condition</u> where the blood <u>doesn't clot easily</u> because a <u>clotting factor</u> can't be made by the body — this missing clotting factor can be injected.

Blood Type is Important in Transfusions

1) If you're in an accident or having surgery, you may lose a lot of blood — this needs to be replaced by a <u>blood transfusion</u> (using blood from a <u>blood donor</u>). But you can't just use any old blood...

2) People have different <u>blood groups</u> or <u>types</u> — you can be any one of: A, B, O or AB. These letters refer to the type of <u>antigens</u> on the surface of a person's red blood cells. (An antigen is a substance that can trigger a response from a person's <u>immune system</u>.)

3) Red blood cells can have <u>A or B antigens</u> (or <u>neither</u>, or <u>both</u>) on their surface.

4) And blood plasma can contain <u>anti-A or anti-B antibodies</u>. (Plasma's the pale liquid in blood that actually carries all the different bits — e.g. the blood cells, antibodies, hormones, etc.)

5) If an anti-A antibody meets an A antigen, the blood clots up and it all goes <u>hideously wrong</u>. Same thing when an anti-B antibody meets a B antigen. (This is <u>agglutination</u> — a fancy name for 'clumping together'. The <u>antibodies</u> are acting as <u>agglutinins</u> — or 'things that make stuff clump together'.)

6) This table should make everything lovely and clear...

Blood Group	Antigens	Antibodies	Can give blood to	Can get blood from
A	A	anti-B	A and AB	A and O
B	B	anti-A	B and AB	B and O
AB	A, B	none	only AB	anyone
O	none	anti-A, anti-B	anyone	only O

For example, '<u>O blood</u>' can be given to <u>anyone</u> — there are <u>no antigens</u> on the blood cells, so any <u>anti-A</u> or <u>anti-B antibodies</u> have nothing to 'attack'.

I think I need an information transfusion... from this book to my brain...

You might get asked a question on <u>who</u> can donate blood to <u>who</u> (or vice versa) in the exam. Just look at what blood type the donor is and think about what <u>antigens</u> and <u>antibodies</u> they have in their blood. It's <u>hard</u>, and you need to think <u>carefully</u> about it (I do anyway), but it does make sense.

Organ Replacements and Donation

If an organ's severely damaged, it can be replaced by an artificial part or a donated natural organ. Wow.

Organs Can be Replaced by Living or Dead Donors

1) Living donors can donate whole (or parts of) certain organs. For example, you can live with just one of your two kidneys and donate the other, or you can donate a piece of your liver. To be a living donor you must be fit and healthy, over 18, and usually a close family member (for a good tissue match).
2) Organs from people who have recently died, or who are brain dead, can also be transplanted.
3) To donate any organ, you must meet the criteria for heart donors on p.45.
4) But there's a big shortage of donors...

The UK has a shortage of organs available for donation.
- You can join the NHS Organ Donor Register to show you're willing to donate organs after you die. However, doctors still need your family's consent before they can use the organs for a transplant.
- Some people say it should be made easier for doctors to use the organs of people who have died. One suggestion is to have an 'opt-out' system instead — this means anyone's organs can be used unless the person has registered to say they don't want them to be donated.

5) Success rates of transplants depend on a lot of things — e.g. the type of organ (e.g. the heart is riskier than a kidney), the age of the patient, the skill of the surgeon, etc.
6) But transplants involve major surgery — and even if all goes well, there can be problems with rejection or taking immunosuppressive drugs (see p.45).

There are Issues Surrounding Organ Donation

Like with lots of medical advances, there are ethical issues...

1) Some people think for religious reasons that a person's body should be buried intact (so giving organs is wrong). Others think life or death is up to God (so receiving organs is wrong).
2) Others worry that doctors might not save them if they're critically ill and their organs are needed for transplant. There are safeguards in place that should prevent this though.
3) There are also worries that people may get pressured into being a 'living donor' (e.g. donating a kidney to a close relative). But doctors try to ensure that it's always the donor's personal choice.

Some Mechanical Replacements are Used Outside the Body

1) Mechanical (artificial) replacements can also be used. These don't have the same problems with rejection — they have a whole new set of problems instead (flick back to p.45 for more info).
2) Sometimes, temporary mechanical replacements are needed to keep someone alive. This could be for anything from a few hours (e.g. during an operation), to several months or even years (e.g. if they're waiting for a suitable organ donor). For example...

- A heart-lung machine keeps a patient's blood oxygenated and pumping during heart or lung surgery.
- A kidney dialysis machine can filter a patient's blood (e.g. while they wait for a kidney transplant). See p.85 for more info.
- In the old days, an iron lung could be used to ventilate a patient's lungs if they stopped breathing (though nowadays modern ventilators are used).

I think I need a brain transplant to learn all this lot...

Did you know... that if you transplant a piece of a liver it can actually grow back to normal size within a few weeks. Impressive. Changing the subject slightly... one donor can donate several organs — e.g. their heart, kidneys, liver, lungs, pancreas... And on top of that, other tissues (e.g. skin, bone, tendons, corneas...) can also be donated. It's absolutely amazing really, when you think about it.

The Respiratory System

The respiratory system is the posh name for the breathing system — all things to do with the lungs.

Breathing In and Out Uses Muscles

Inspiration (or Breathing In)...

1) Your intercostal muscles (between the ribs) and diaphragm (the muscle beneath the lungs) contract, and increase the volume of the thorax (the bit of your body containing your lungs).

2) A pleural membrane inside the thorax pulls on another pleural membrane attached to the lungs, expanding them — this decreases the pressure inside your lungs, and draws air in.

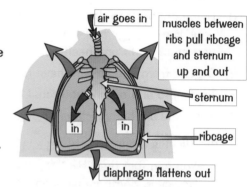

...and Expiration (or Breathing Out)

1) Intercostals and diaphragm relax.
2) The thorax volume decreases.
3) Air is forced out.

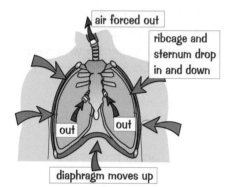

Lung Capacity Can be Measured with a Spirometer

Doctors measure lung capacity using a machine called a spirometer — it can help diagnose and monitor lung diseases.

The patient breathes into the machine (through a tube) for a few minutes, and the volume of air that is breathed in and out is measured and plotted on a graph (called a spirogram) — like this one...

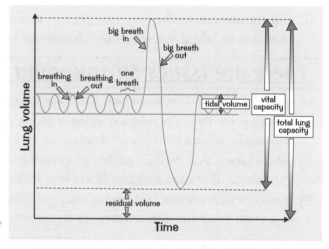

1) The total volume of air you can fit in your lungs is your total lung capacity (usually about 6 litres).

2) The volume of air you breathe in (or out) in one normal breath is called your tidal volume.

3) Even if you try to breathe out really hard there's always some air left (just over a litre) in your lungs to make sure that they stay open — this is called the residual volume.

4) Total lung capacity minus residual volume gives you vital capacity — the amount of usable air.

Cilia and Mucus Protect the Lungs

1) The respiratory tract (trachea and bronchi) is lined with mucus and cilia (little hairs) which catch dust and microbes before they reach the lungs.

2) The cilia beat, pushing microbe-filled mucus out of the lungs as phlegm.

3) Sometimes the microbes get past the body's defences and cause infection. The lungs are particularly prone to infections because they're a dead end — microbes can't easily be flushed out.

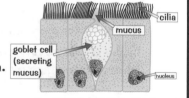

Spirograms... aren't they those fancy drawing machines...

If the values on a spirogram are low the person might have a lung disease. If the tidal volume increases (i.e. if they're breathing deeper), then they're probably exercising. A spirogram can also be used to calculate breathing rate (by counting the number of breaths in a minute). Simple really.

The Respiratory System

All animals need to take oxygen in (for <u>respiration</u>) and get carbon dioxide out (CO_2 is a <u>waste</u> gas — it needs to be <u>removed</u>). How this happens varies loads though.

In Humans, Gaseous Exchange Happens in the Lungs

In humans, air enters the body through the mouth or nose, then goes into the <u>trachea</u> (windpipe). Then...

- The trachea splits into two tubes called '<u>bronchi</u>' (each one is '<u>a bronchus</u>'), one going to each lung.
- The bronchi split into progressively smaller tubes called <u>bronchioles</u>, and at the end of the line there are small bags called <u>alveoli</u> where the gaseous exchange takes place.

To make gaseous exchange as <u>efficient</u> as possible the alveoli have:
- a very <u>large surface area</u>,
- a <u>moist surface</u> to help oxygen and carbon dioxide dissolve,
- a <u>thin lining</u> so gases don't have to diffuse very far,
- a <u>good blood supply</u>.

See pages 40-41 for more.

Don't forget that the gases move in and out by <u>diffusion</u> (see p.39).

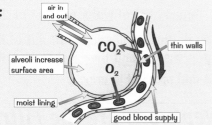

air in and out

CO_2

O_2

alveoli increase surface area

thin walls

moist lining

good blood supply

In other organisms, the oxygen and the carbon dioxide are exchanged differently...

1) <u>Adult</u> amphibians have simple <u>lungs</u>, but their <u>skin</u> also plays an important part in <u>gaseous exchange</u>.

2) <u>Oxygen</u> moves into the animal and <u>carbon dioxide</u> moves out through the <u>skin</u> (as well as via the <u>lungs</u>). To help with this, an adult amphibian's skin has to be kept <u>moist</u>.

3) However, this means the skin can't be <u>waterproof</u>. This lack of waterproofing means the amphibian would <u>lose</u> too much water if it lived in a <u>dry</u> environment.

1) In <u>fish</u>, <u>gas exchange</u> occurs at the <u>gills</u> (slits near the side of the head). A constant supply of <u>oxygen-rich</u> water flows through the open mouth of the fish, and is then forced through the <u>gill slits</u> (which are <u>highly folded</u> to increase the <u>surface area</u>).

2) Water helps <u>support</u> the gills — it keeps the gill folds separated from each other. If fish weren't in water their gills would stick together and they would suffocate (which is why <u>fish</u> can <u>only</u> breathe when they're <u>in water</u>).

Lung Disease Can be Caused by Lots of Things

1) <u>Industrial materials</u> e.g. <u>asbestos</u>. Asbestos can cause cancers, as well as a disease called <u>asbestosis</u> (where lung tissue is scarred, causing breathlessness and even death). Asbestos used to be used as an insulator in roofs, floors, furnaces, etc. Its use is more tightly controlled now.

2) <u>Genetic causes</u> e.g. <u>cystic fibrosis</u> is an inherited lung condition. A single defective gene causes the lungs to produce a really thick, sticky <u>mucus</u> that clogs up the lungs — this makes breathing difficult and can lead to life-threatening infections.

3) <u>Lifestyle causes</u> e.g. <u>smoking</u> can cause <u>lung cancer</u> (see p.8). This is where <u>cells</u> divide <u>out of control</u>, forming a <u>tumour</u>. The abnormal cells can get into the blood and cause tumours elsewhere.

4) <u>Asthma</u> Asthma affects around 1 in 12 adults in the UK. Asthmatics' lungs are <u>overly sensitive</u> to certain things (e.g. pet hair, pollen, dust, smoke...). When they encounter these things the <u>muscles</u> around the airways <u>constrict</u>, narrowing the airways and making it hard to breathe (an <u>asthma attack</u>). Symptoms of an attack are <u>shortness of breath</u>, <u>coughing</u>, <u>wheezing</u> and a <u>tight chest</u>. When symptoms appear a muscle relaxant drug is inhaled (from an <u>inhaler</u>) to open up the airways. Some people also take drugs to stop attacks happening in the first place (but there's <u>no actual cure</u>.)

What did the fish say when it swam into a wall? Dam...

Different animals do 'gaseous exchange' in different ways, though the <u>basic aim</u> is always the <u>same</u> — to get oxygen <u>into</u> the blood and carbon dioxide <u>out</u>. But all these methods can restrict animals (including us) to a certain kind of <u>habitat</u>. Learn this stuff, or you'll be a fish out of water on exam day.

Waste Disposal

The kidney is involved in <u>excretion</u> of wastes from the body. (Don't get <u>excretion</u> and <u>defecation</u> mixed up — excretion is getting rid of waste products from the body, defecation is pooing.)

The Kidneys are Excretion Organs

The <u>kidneys</u> perform <u>three main roles</u>:

1) <u>Removal of urea</u> from the blood. Urea is produced in the <u>liver</u> from <u>excess amino acids</u>.

2) <u>Adjustment of ion levels</u> in the blood.

3) <u>Adjustment of water content</u> of the blood.

They do this by <u>filtering</u> stuff out of the blood under <u>high pressure</u>, and then <u>reabsorbing</u> the useful things. The end product is <u>urine</u>.

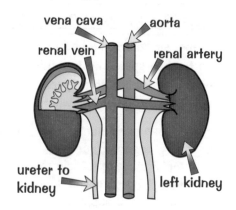

Nephrons are the Filtration Units in the Kidneys

1) Ultrafiltration:

1) A <u>high pressure</u> is built up which squeezes <u>water</u>, <u>urea</u>, <u>ions</u> and <u>glucose</u> out of the blood and into the <u>capsule</u>.

2) <u>Membranes</u> between the blood vessels and the capsule act like <u>filters</u>, so <u>big</u> molecules like <u>proteins</u> and <u>blood cells</u> are <u>not</u> squeezed out. They stay in the blood.

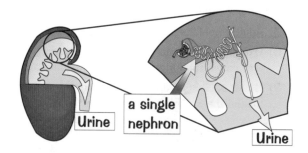

2) Reabsorption:

As the liquid flows along the nephron, <u>useful</u> substances are <u>reabsorbed</u>:

1) <u>All</u> the <u>sugar</u> is reabsorbed. (This involves the process of <u>active transport</u> against the concentration gradient — see p.65.)

2) <u>Sufficient ions</u> are reabsorbed (again, using active transport). Excess ions are not.

3) <u>Sufficient water</u> is reabsorbed, according to the level of the hormone <u>ADH</u> (see next page).

Enlarged View of a Single Nephron

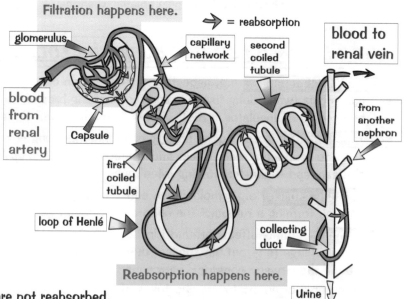

3) Release of wastes:

Urea, excess ions and excess water are not reabsorbed. These continue out of the <u>nephron</u>, into the ureter and down to the <u>bladder</u> as <u>urine</u>.

Reabsorb those facts and excrete the excess...

On average, the kidneys filter 180 litres of blood a day (you only have 4-6 litres of blood in your body — it just goes through the kidneys about <u>40 times</u>). And the kidneys excrete 1.5 litres of urine a day — so that's 547.5 litres of wee a year... that's five baths full... not that I'm suggesting you put it there.

Waste Disposal

Waste disposal isn't the easiest or most interesting topic in the world, I admit.

Water Content is Controlled by the Kidneys

1) The amount of water reabsorbed in the kidney nephrons is controlled by a hormone called anti-diuretic hormone (ADH).

2) The brain monitors the water content of the blood and instructs the pituitary gland to release ADH into the blood according to how much is needed.

3) The whole process of water content regulation is controlled by a mechanism called negative feedback (see page 13). This means that if the water content gets too high or too low a mechanism will be triggered that brings it back to normal.

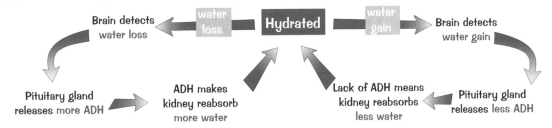

Your Urine isn't Always the Same

The amount and concentration of urine produced depends on three main things:

1) Heat When it's hot you sweat (which evaporates, cooling down the skin). Sweat contains water, so... sweating causes water loss.

This means the kidney will reabsorb more water into the blood. This leaves only a small amount of excess water that needs to be got rid of — so only a small amount of quite concentrated urine will be produced.

See page 13 for more on sweating.

2) Exercise Exercise makes you hot, so you sweat to cool down. This produces the same effect as heat — a concentrated, small volume of urine.

3) Water Intake Not drinking enough water will produce concentrated urine (since there'll be little excess water to 'dilute' the other wastes). Drinking lots of water will produce lots of dilute urine.

Dialysis Filters the Blood Mechanically

1) Patients who have kidney failure can't filter their blood properly — but a dialysis machine can be used to filter their blood for them.

2) Dialysis has to be done regularly to keep dissolved substances at the right concentrations, and to remove waste.

3) Dialysis fluid has the same concentration of salts and glucose as blood plasma (which means those aren't removed from the blood).

dialysis fluid out

selectively permeable barrier

dialysis fluid in

Waste products diffuse out into dialysis fluid

from person

back to person

4) The barrier is permeable to things like ions and waste substances, but not big molecules like proteins (just like the membranes in the kidney). So.. the waste substances (such as urea) and excess ions and water from the blood move across the membrane into the dialysis fluid.

Simon says touch urea... actually don't...

Kidney failure patients often have high blood pressure because diseased kidneys can't control the water content of the blood. This excess water is removed during dialysis (up to 5 litres of fluid can be removed in one session). Dialysis is normally done three times a week for about 4 hours at a time — not fun.

The Menstrual Cycle

The monthly release of an egg from a woman's ovaries and the build-up and breakdown of the lining in the womb (uterus) is called the menstrual cycle.

The Menstrual Cycle Has Four Stages

Stage 1 Day 1 is when the bleeding starts. The uterus lining breaks down for about four days.

Stage 2 The lining of the uterus builds up again, from day 4 to day 14, into a thick spongy layer of blood vessels ready to receive a fertilised egg.

Stage 3 An egg is developed and then released from the ovary at about day 14.

Stage 4 The wall is then maintained for about 14 days, until day 28. If no fertilised egg has landed on the uterus wall by day 28 then the spongy lining starts to break down again and the whole cycle starts over.

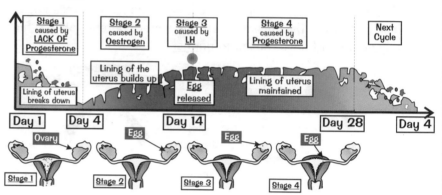

It's Controlled by Four Hormones

1. FSH (follicle-stimulating hormone)
1) Produced in the pituitary gland.
2) Causes an egg to develop in one of the ovaries.
3) Stimulates the ovaries to produce oestrogen.

2. Oestrogen
1) Produced in the ovaries.
2) Causes the lining of the uterus to thicken and grow.
3) Stimulates the production of LH (which causes the release of an egg) and inhibits production of FSH.

3. LH (luteinising hormone)
1) Produced by the pituitary gland.
2) Stimulates the release of an egg at day 14.

4. Progesterone
1) Produced in the ovaries.
2) Maintains the lining of the uterus. When the level of progesterone falls, the lining breaks down.

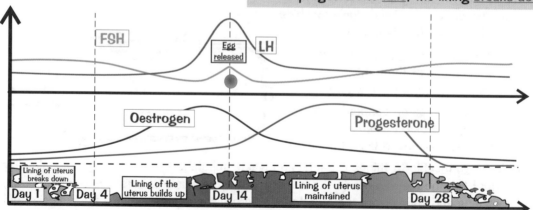

There will be no joke on this page! There is NOTHING funny about the menstrual cycle.*

It's a good idea to get your head around the two diagrams on this page cos they're likely to come up in the exam. Make sure you understand which hormones cause:
a) the thickening of the uterus lining, b) egg release, c) the maintenance of the uterus lining.

Infertility Treatment

Sometimes couples who can't conceive naturally seek medical treatment to help nature along a bit.

Infertility Can be Treated in Different Ways

1) ARTIFICIAL INSEMINATION (AI) — this is where a man's <u>sperm</u> is placed into a woman's uterus without having sex. It's used if there's some kind of problem with the sperm <u>reaching</u> the egg, or if the man suffers from certain kinds of infertility. Sperm from a <u>donor</u> can also be used if necessary.

2) FSH INJECTIONS — some women have <u>very low levels</u> of the hormone <u>FSH</u>. This means that their <u>eggs don't develop</u> properly, so they can't get pregnant. <u>FSH injections</u> help to increase fertility.

3) IN VITRO FERTILISATION (IVF) — this is where a woman's eggs are <u>fertilised outside the body</u>. The woman is given hormones to stimulate egg production. Several eggs are then collected and mixed with the man's sperm, and a few fertilised eggs are implanted back into the woman's uterus.

So... for IVF you need <u>sperm</u>, <u>eggs</u> and <u>a healthy uterus</u>. Any of these can come from <u>someone else</u>:

- Some women can't produce eggs (e.g. because of damaged ovaries or blocked Fallopian tubes). But they can still have a baby by using <u>donated eggs</u> (though the woman who gives birth won't be the <u>genetic</u> parent of the child).
- Some women can produce eggs but always <u>miscarry</u>. The couple's fertilised eggs can be implanted into <u>another woman</u> (called a <u>surrogate</u> mother), who gives birth to their baby.

4) OVARY TRANSPLANTS — some women don't have ovaries (e.g. due to surgery for ovarian cancer) or they have damaged ones that don't produce any eggs (again, often due to cancer treatment). A relatively new way to treat this is to <u>transplant</u> a <u>healthy ovary</u> donated by someone else. It's pretty rare at the moment but could become a more common treatment.

Not Everyone Agrees with Fertility Treatment

Fertility treatment can give an infertile couple <u>a child</u> — a pretty obvious <u>benefit</u>. But some people argue <u>against</u> using some of these fertility treatments, either for ethical or practical reasons.

1) There's the argument that it's just <u>not natural</u> — if you can't have a child, it wasn't meant to be.

2) In <u>IVF</u> not all the fertilised eggs are implanted back into the woman. Some people think that <u>throwing away</u> these extra fertilised eggs (embryos) is <u>denying a life</u> and so morally wrong.

3) IVF increases the chance of <u>multiple pregnancies</u> (e.g. twins). This can be a <u>danger</u> to the <u>mother's health</u> and possibly a <u>financial burden</u> to the parents.

4) What happens if the surrogate mother <u>doesn't</u> want to <u>give up</u> the child?

Foetuses Can be Screened to See If They're Healthy

Doctors can <u>screen</u> a foetus for <u>genetic disorders</u> (see p.19) before it's born. They can check for various problems, e.g. <u>Down's syndrome</u> and <u>cystic fibrosis</u>. There are two main methods used...

1) <u>Amniocentesis</u> — doctors use a long needle to remove some of the <u>fluid</u> that surrounds the baby. This contains skin cells, and the <u>DNA</u> in these can be analysed (but there's a <u>slight risk</u> to the foetus).

2) Another method (chorionic villus sampling) involves taking a sample of the <u>placenta</u>. It's <u>more risky</u> than amniocentesis but can be done <u>earlier on</u> in the pregnancy.

Like with infertility treatments, there are <u>ethical</u> issues surrounding screening. For example...

- If the foetus has a genetic defect, is it right to have an <u>abortion</u>?
- Or might <u>minor</u> defects such as a cleft lip become grounds for abortion?

"AI" — I didn't expect an infertility treatment film to be so good...

Around 8000 babies are born in the UK by IVF every year. Wow. Now then... prenatal diagnosis isn't done on <u>every</u> pregnant woman — just those at risk of having babies with genetic defects.

Growth

Growth is pretty important. Without growth, we'd still be an egg-sperm fusion, and that's about it.

Growth *is* Influenced *by* Many Things

Growth happens when <u>cells divide</u> (by <u>mitosis</u>, see p.46) — producing new cells <u>identical</u> to the originals.

1) The size an adult reaches is mainly due to <u>genetic</u> factors, but it can be influenced by <u>external</u> factors.

   E.g., **1) Diet** is important, especially for <u>children</u> who are growing. A <u>poor diet</u>, particularly if it's low in <u>proteins</u> (needed to make new cells) or <u>minerals</u> (for bone growth), may mean that a child doesn't grow as much as its genes would allow.

   2) Exercise can also affect growth. Exercise builds <u>muscle</u>, and weight-bearing exercise can increase <u>bone mass</u>. Exercise also stimulates the release of <u>growth hormone</u>.

   > <u>Growth hormone</u> is produced by the <u>pituitary gland</u>, which is situated on the underside of the <u>brain</u>. It produces many hormones with a variety of effects, but <u>growth hormone</u> stimulates general <u>growth</u> (especially in the <u>long bones</u>).

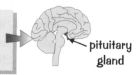
pituitary gland

2) Sometimes <u>hormonal</u> or <u>genetic</u> factors affect growth. <u>Gigantism</u> (extreme <u>height</u>) is often the result of a <u>tumour</u> of the pituitary in <u>childhood</u>, which causes too much <u>growth hormone</u> to be produced. <u>Dwarfism</u> (extreme short stature) is caused by <u>genetic</u> factors, and results in <u>stunted</u> bone growth.

A Baby's Growth *is* Monitored

1) A baby's growth is regularly <u>monitored</u> after birth to make sure it's growing <u>normally</u>. Three measurements are taken — <u>length</u>, <u>mass</u> and <u>head circumference</u>. These results are plotted on average growth charts, like this...

2) The chart shows a number of '<u>percentiles</u>'. E.g. the <u>50th percentile</u> shows the mass that <u>50%</u> of babies will have reached at a certain age.

3) Babies <u>vary</u> in size, so doctors aren't usually concerned unless a baby's size is above the <u>98th</u> percentile or below the <u>2nd</u> percentile, or if there's an <u>inconsistent pattern</u> (e.g. a small baby with a very large head).

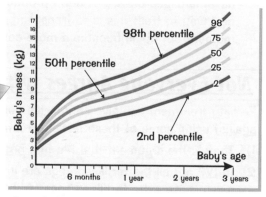

Growth charts can pick up things like obesity, malnutrition, dwarfism, water on the brain, and so on.

People Live Longer Than They Used To

<u>Life expectancy</u> in the UK has <u>increased</u> loads over the last century... There are many reasons for this, such as:

1) <u>medical advances</u> mean previously fatal conditions can be <u>treated</u>,
2) places of <u>work</u> and <u>housing</u> are much <u>safer</u> and <u>healthier</u>,
3) people are <u>better off</u> and can afford a healthier diet and lifestyle,
4) there's much more <u>information</u> available about <u>health issues</u>.

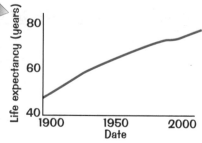

There are problems that come with people living longer, however. (No one's saying it's a bad thing — only that we need to think about it...)

1) The population grows, leading to possible <u>shortages</u> of housing and more environmental <u>pollution</u>.
2) The number of <u>older people</u> increases, and the state might not be able to give <u>pensions</u> to everyone.
3) Older people have more <u>medical problems</u> and need more care, increasing costs to the <u>taxpayer</u>.

From cell division to babies to old-age pensions — what a page...

It's a big worry, this whole people living longer lark. By the time you're a senior citizen, you'll have to work until you're 70 as there just won't be enough money to give everyone pensions. <u>Poor you</u>.

Revision Summary for Module B5

It's the end of the section. And that can only mean one thing. Yep... it's time for a good ol' revision summary. That's right — it's time to see how much you've learned in this section. Which had better be everything, frankly — or you're going to have to go back and learn the stuff again — properly, this time. So heads down, eyes open — and get ready to see how much revision you need, or don't need, to do...

1) List three advantages of an internal skeleton over an external skeleton.

2) Why is it unwise to move someone with a broken bone?

3) Describe how a ball and socket joint works.

4) What happens to the lower arm when the triceps contracts?

5) Describe the circulatory system of humans. How is it different from the circulatory system of fish?

6) Describe one of Galen's theories which was disproved by Harvey.

7) Name the two clusters of pacemaker cells in the heart. What do they do?

8) What does ECG stand for? Describe what a healthy person's ECG should look like.

9) Explain what's going wrong if someone has a hole in the heart.

10) List five lifestyle 'dangers' which may cause an increased likelihood of cardiovascular disease.

11) What exactly is happening when blood clots? How might your diet affect the way your blood clots?

12) Explain what would happen if a person with type A blood was given a transfusion of type B blood.

13) To donate an organ, you must meet four criteria. What are they?

14) Name three types of mechanical organ replacements. What do they do?

15) Describe what happens to the intercostal muscles and diaphragm when you breathe in and out.

16) Explain the difference between fish, amphibians and humans in terms of gaseous exchange.

17) List the four main causes of lung disease. Which of these is the most likely to result in lung cancer?

18) What machine would a doctor use to measure lung capacity? Why would you want to measure it?

19) Describe the three main roles of the kidneys.

20) Explain how a kidney works.

21) Describe three things that affect the amount and concentration of urine produced.

22) How does a dialysis machine work? Which substances does it remove from the blood?

23) Briefly describe what happens in each of the four stages of the menstrual cycle.

24) Which four hormones control the menstrual cycle? What exactly do they do?

25) Describe four types of fertility treatment. Which could help a single woman get pregnant?

26) List five reasons why people may argue that fertility treatment is wrong.

27) Name the two main methods of foetal screening.
Explain two ethical issues to do with foetal screening.

28) How can diet and exercise affect a person's growth?

29) What three measurements do doctors make to check a baby is growing normally?

30) Why are people living longer these days? What problems is this trend going to cause?

Bacteria

Bacteria are a type of micro-organism. They're tiny — typical bacteria are just a few microns (thousandths of a millimetre) wide. But <u>despite their small size</u>, they can have a <u>mighty effect</u> on humans...

Bacterial Cells are Usually Smaller and Simpler than Animal Cells

1) This table shows how bacterial cells <u>compare</u> to plant and animal cells.

2) Bacterial cells <u>don't</u> have a <u>proper nucleus</u> like plant and animal cells do. They have <u>bacterial DNA</u> to <u>control</u> the <u>cell's activities</u> and <u>replication</u>, but the DNA just floats about in the cytoplasm.

3) They also <u>don't</u> have any <u>mitochondria</u>, <u>chloroplasts</u> or a <u>vacuole</u>.

4) They have a <u>cell wall</u> to <u>keep their shape</u> and <u>stop them bursting</u>. This isn't the same kind of cell wall found in a plant though.

Feature	Animal Cell	Plant Cell	Bacterial Cell
Nucleus	✓	✓	✕
Cell membrane	✓	✓	✓
Mitochondria	✓	✓	✕
Cell Wall	✕	✓	✓
Chloroplasts	✕	✓	✕
Vacuole	✕	✓	✕
Extras	None	None	Flagellum

5) They sometimes have a <u>flagellum</u> (tail) to help them <u>move</u>.

6) They come in <u>4 shapes</u>: <u>rods</u>, <u>curved rods</u>, <u>spheres</u> and <u>spirals</u>.

7) Bacteria can <u>consume</u> a <u>huge range</u> of <u>organic nutrients</u> from their surroundings. This provides them with <u>energy</u>. Some types of bacteria can even produce their own nutrients.

8) This means they can <u>survive</u> pretty much <u>anywhere</u> — in soil, water, air, in your house, in the human body and in food.

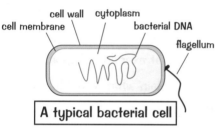

cell wall   cytoplasm
cell membrane   bacterial DNA
flagellum

A typical bacterial cell

Bacteria Reproduce by Asexual Reproduction

1) Bacteria reproduce by <u>asexual reproduction</u> — they're <u>clones</u> of each other. They reproduce by a process called <u>binary fission</u> (a posh way of saying 'they split in two').

2) Bacteria <u>reproduce very quickly</u>. If <u>disease-causing bacteria</u> enter your body, they can reproduce and <u>cause disease</u> before your body has a chance to respond.

3) Bacteria <u>reproduce more quickly</u> in <u>certain conditions</u>. Generally, if it's <u>warm</u> and they have a good source of <u>nutrients</u> then they will grow better. This is why it's important to <u>store food carefully</u>. If you leave some meat on a warm kitchen top, bacteria on the meat will reproduce very quickly and cause it to <u>spoil</u> (go off). But if you put the same meat in the fridge, then the <u>cold temperature</u> will <u>slow down</u> the bacteria's reproduction and it won't spoil as quickly.

We Can Use Bacteria to Make Useful Things Like Yoghurt

Bacteria can be <u>useful</u> to humans. Here's how they're used to make <u>yoghurt</u>:

1) The <u>equipment</u> is <u>sterilised</u> to kill off any unwanted micro-organisms.

2) Then the milk is <u>pasteurised</u> (heated up to 72 °C for 15 seconds) — again to kill off any unwanted micro-organisms. Then the milk's <u>cooled</u>.

3) A <u>starter culture</u> of bacteria is added. The mixture is <u>incubated</u> (heated to about 40 °C) in a vessel called a <u>fermenter</u> (see p.95). The bacteria ferment the <u>lactose sugar</u> in the milk into <u>lactic acid</u>. The lactic acid causes the milk to <u>clot</u> and <u>solidify</u> into <u>yoghurt</u>.

4) A <u>sample</u> is taken to make sure it's at the right consistency. Then <u>flavours</u> (e.g. fruit) and <u>colours</u> are sometimes added and the yoghurt is <u>packaged</u>.

YOGHURT

Yoghurt — bacteria and gone-off milk... mmm...yummy...

Bacteria are also used to make <u>cheese</u>, <u>vinegar</u>, <u>silage</u> (for animal feed) and <u>compost</u> (for your garden). Bacteria that can make Belgian chocolates, caviar and profiteroles haven't been discovered yet...

Harmful Micro-organisms

There are different kinds of micro-organism, e.g. bacteria, viruses, fungi and protozoa. Some are useful, while others are pretty harmful if you get infected. This page focuses on the nasty ones...

Micro-organisms That Cause Disease are Called Pathogens

1) Bacteria cause tuberculosis (a lung disease), septic wounds, cholera and food poisoning.
   - Food poisoning is often caused by the bacteria Salmonella or Escherichia coli (E. coli). You get infected by eating food that has been contaminated with these bacteria.
   - Cholera is caused by bacteria called Vibrio cholerae. You get infected by drinking water that's been contaminated with sewage (nice). It isn't a big problem in the developed world but it kills many people in underdeveloped countries where sanitation is poor.
2) Viruses cause influenza (flu), chickenpox and smallpox.
   - You get infected with flu by inhaling airborne viruses. These viruses are spread by infected people when they cough or sneeze. You can also get it by touching an infected surface then touching your mouth or nose.
3) Fungi cause athlete's foot (which makes your feet smelly and itchy).
4) Protozoa (single-celled organisms) cause malaria and dysentery (diarrhoea).
   - Dysentery is often caused by a protozoan called Entamoeba. You get infected by drinking contaminated water. Like cholera, it's more common in less economically developed countries.

These are just examples of the kinds of things that micro-organisms cause.

There Are Four Stages in an Infectious Disease

1 Firstly the micro-organism has to get into the body to cause an infection. There are four main ways they can do it:

- Through the nose, e.g. airborne micro-organisms like the influenza virus are breathed in.
- Through the mouth, e.g. contaminated food and water causes food poisoning and cholera.
- Through the skin, e.g. cuts, insect bites and infected needles can introduce a pathogen into the body directly or they can breach the skin, allowing micro-organisms on the skin to get in.
- Through sexual contact, e.g. the HIV virus that causes AIDS can get into the body this way.

2 Once the micro-organism is in the body it reproduces rapidly, producing many more micro-organisms.

3 The micro-organisms then produce toxins (poisonous substances) which damage cells and tissues.

4 The toxins cause symptoms of infection, e.g. pain, diarrhoea and stomach cramps. Your immune system's reaction to the infection can also cause symptoms, e.g. fever. The time between exposure to the micro-organism and the development of symptoms is called the incubation period.

Poor Sanitation is Linked to a High Incidence of Disease

1) The incidence of a disease is the number of new cases that occurs in a population in a certain time.
2) Good sanitation and public health measures are linked to a low incidence of disease. A clean water supply, good sewage works, public health education and clean hospitals prevent the spread of disease.
3) Poor sanitation is linked with a high incidence of disease. E.g. a high incidence of food poisoning, dysentery and cholera might be caused by a lack of clean water or a knackered sewage system. A high incidence of septicaemia (a bacterial blood infection) might be caused by poor hygiene in hospital operating theatres or a lack of education about cleaning cuts properly.
4) Developing countries are less likely to be able to afford good sanitation and public health measures.

Incidence of revision is increasing due to exams...

Don't forget that some of these nasty bacterial infections can be treated with antibiotics. You shouldn't overuse antibiotics though — you'll increase levels of bacterial resistance. The little blighters.

Harmful Micro-organisms

This is a page of two halves. First there's a <u>depressing</u> section about the spread of disease after natural disasters. Then there's a <u>more cheerful</u> bit about the treatment of disease.

Diseases Often Spread Rapidly After Natural Disasters

Natural disasters like earthquakes and hurricanes can damage the infrastructure of an area, and completely <u>disrupt health services</u>. In these conditions <u>disease can spread rapidly</u> among the population.

1) Some natural disasters <u>damage sewage systems</u> and <u>water supplies</u>. This can result in <u>contaminated drinking water</u> containing the <u>micro-organisms</u> that <u>cause diseases</u> like cholera and dysentery.

2) <u>Transport systems</u> can be damaged — making it difficult for health services to reach people in need.

3) <u>Electricity supplies</u> are also often <u>damaged</u> by natural disasters. This means that <u>food goes off quickly</u> because refrigerators can't work — this can lead to an increase in <u>food poisoning</u>.

Antiseptics and Antibiotics Help Control Diseases

1) <u>Antiseptics</u> and <u>antibiotics</u> are chemicals that <u>destroy bacteria</u> or <u>stop them growing</u>.

2) Antiseptics are used <u>outside</u> the body to help to <u>clean wounds</u> and <u>surfaces</u>. They're used to <u>prevent infection</u> rather than treat it. Plenty of household products contain antiseptics, e.g. bathroom cleaners. Antiseptics are also used in <u>hospitals</u> and surgeries to try to prevent infections like MRSA.

3) Antibiotics are drugs used <u>inside</u> the body, usually taken as a pill or injected. They're used to treat patients who are <u>already infected</u>. They <u>only kill bacteria</u> though — viruses aren't affected by them.

Pasteur, Lister and Fleming All Improved Disease Treatment

Louis Pasteur (1822-1895) came up with the germ theory of disease

Until the 19th century people didn't understand how diseases were caused or spread. People used to think that diseases <u>spontaneously appeared</u> from nowhere. The scientist Louis Pasteur argued that there are <u>microbes</u> (also called 'germs' or 'micro-organisms') in the <u>air</u> which <u>cause disease</u> and <u>decomposition</u>.

Pasteur carried out <u>experiments</u> to prove this theory, e.g.

1) He heated <u>broth</u> in two flasks, <u>both</u> of which were left <u>open</u> to the air. However, one of the flasks had a <u>curved neck</u> so that bacteria in the air would settle in the loop, and <u>not get through</u> to the broth.

2) The broth in the flask with the <u>curved neck</u> stayed <u>fresh</u>, proving that it was the <u>microbes</u> and not the air causing it to go off.

Flask 1: Air and microbes get in

Flask 2: Air gets in, but microbes can't

microbes settle here

boiled broth

Joseph Lister (1827-1912) was the first doctor to use antiseptics in surgery

1) When Lister first started working as a surgeon, hospital conditions were pretty <u>unhygienic</u>. Nearly half of patients undergoing surgery died from <u>infections</u> of their wounds, known as 'hospital gangrene' or '<u>sepsis</u>'.

2) Lister's <u>observations</u> of wounds led him to think <u>sepsis</u> was a <u>type of decomposition</u>. He knew about Pasteur's work on <u>microbes in the air</u>. He realised he needed to kill microbes that were <u>getting into wounds</u> from the <u>air</u>.

3) Lister began to <u>treat</u> and <u>dress wounds</u> using the <u>antiseptic carbolic acid</u>. This killed the bacteria in the wounds and <u>prevented sepsis</u>. Gradually, Lister's techniques were taken up by the rest of the medical profession.

Alexander Fleming (1881-1955) discovered the antibiotic penicillin in 1928 — by accident

1) Fleming was clearing out some plates containing <u>bacteria</u>. He noticed that one of the plates of bacteria also had <u>mould</u> on it and the <u>area around the mould</u> was <u>free of the bacteria</u>.

2) He concluded that the <u>mould</u> (called Penicillium notatum) on the plate must be producing a <u>substance</u> that <u>killed the bacteria</u> — this substance was <u>penicillin</u>.

plate

bacteria

mould

area where bacteria have been killed

After Fleming there was no more phlegm-ing...

Fleming used to <u>paint pictures</u> using highly pigmented (coloured) <u>bacteria</u>. At first you wouldn't be able to see the picture. But as the bacteria grew, the picture would gradually appear...

Yeast

This page is all about yeast — a pretty useful micro-organism. It helps us make wine and beer.

Yeast is a Micro-organism

1) Yeast is a type of fungus.
2) It reproduces asexually by a process called budding. A bulge forms on part of the cell and it eventually becomes a daughter cell, identical to the parent.
3) Yeast can be easily stored in a dry condition — e.g. baker's yeast is dry granules.

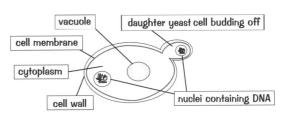

Yeast Can Respire Anaerobically or Aerobically

When yeast respires anaerobically (without oxygen) it produces ethanol, carbon dioxide and energy. This process is called fermentation. Here is the equation for fermentation:

$$glucose \rightarrow ethanol + carbon\ dioxide\ (+ energy)$$
$$C_6H_{12}O_6 \rightarrow 2C_2H_5OH + 2CO_2\ (+ energy)$$

Ethanol is a type of alcohol.

Yeast can also respire aerobically (with oxygen). This releases more energy than anaerobic respiration. Aerobic respiration is the same for yeast as it is for plants and animals:

$$glucose + oxygen \rightarrow carbon\ dioxide + water\ (+ energy)$$

Whether the yeast respire aerobically or anaerobically depends on whether there is oxygen present. If oxygen is present it respires aerobically. If oxygen runs out it switches to anaerobic respiration.

Yeast's Growth Rate Varies Depending on the Conditions

The faster yeast respires, the faster it's able to reproduce. The speed (rate) that yeast respires and reproduces varies depending on factors like: the temperature, amount of glucose, level of toxins and pH.

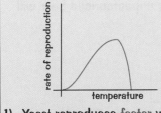

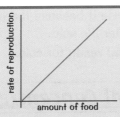

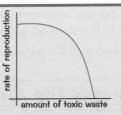

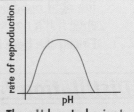

1) Yeast reproduces faster when it's warmer (growth rate doubles for every 10 °C rise in temperature). But if it's too hot the yeast dies.

2) The more food (glucose) there is, the faster the yeast reproduces.

3) Build-up of toxic waste products, e.g. ethanol, slows down reproduction.

4) The pH has to be just right. Too high or low a pH slows down reproduction.

One way of measuring how fast the yeast is reproducing is to measure how much glucose (sugar) it uses up. The faster the yeast reproduces, the more glucose will be used up.

Wastewater Can be Cleaned Up with Yeast

1) Food-processing factories need to get rid of sugary water. They can't just release it into waterways because it would cause pollution. Bacteria in the water would feed on the sugar and reproduce quickly, using up all the oxygen in the water. Other organisms in the water that need oxygen (like fish) die.

2) Yeast can be used to treat the contaminated water before it's released — it uses up the sugar in respiration.

At yeast it's an easy page...

Yeast releases more energy from aerobic respiration than from anaerobic respiration. This means that when there is a good oxygen supply, the yeast has more energy and so reproduces more.

Using Micro-organisms — Brewing

There's more to yeast than cleaning up sugar spills...

We Use Yeast for Brewing Beer and Wine

1 Firstly you need to get the <u>sugar out</u> of the barley or grapes:

BEER

1) Beer is made from <u>grain</u> — usually <u>barley</u>.
2) The barley grains are allowed to <u>germinate</u> for a few days, during which the <u>starch</u> in the grains is broken down into <u>sugar</u> by <u>enzymes</u>. Then the grains are <u>dried</u> in a kiln. This process is called <u>malting</u>.
3) The malted grain is <u>mashed up</u> and water is added to produce a <u>sugary solution</u> with lots of bits in it. This is then sieved to remove the bits.
4) <u>Hops</u> are added to the mixture to give the beer its <u>bitter flavour</u>.

WINE

The grapes are <u>mashed</u> and water is added... a bit simpler than beer making.

Germination is when a seed starts to grow into a new plant.

2
- <u>Yeast</u> is <u>added</u> and the mixture is <u>incubated</u> (heated up). The yeast <u>ferments</u> the <u>sugar</u> into <u>alcohol</u>.
- The fermenting vessels are designed to stop <u>unwanted micro-organisms</u> and <u>air getting in</u>.

   1) The <u>rising concentration of alcohol (ethanol)</u> in the fermentation mixture due to <u>anaerobic respiration</u> eventually starts to <u>kill</u> the <u>yeast</u>. As the yeast dies, fermentation <u>slows</u> down.
   2) Different species of yeast can <u>tolerate different levels of alcohol</u>. Some species can be used to produce strong wine and beer with a <u>high concentration</u> of alcohol.

3
- The beer and wine produced is <u>drawn off</u> through a tap.
- Sometimes chemicals called <u>clarifying agents</u> are added to <u>remove particles</u> and make it <u>clearer</u>.

4
- The <u>beer</u> is then <u>pasteurised</u> — <u>heated</u> to <u>kill any yeast</u> left in the beer and completely stop fermentation. Wine isn't pasteurised — any yeast left in the wine carry on slowly fermenting the sugar. This <u>improves the taste</u> of the wine. Beer also tastes better if it's unpasteurised and aged in the <u>right conditions</u>. But big breweries pasteurise it because there's a <u>risk</u> unpasteurised beer will <u>spoil</u> if it's not stored in the right conditions after it's sold.
- Finally the <u>beer</u> is <u>casked</u> and the <u>wine</u> is <u>bottled</u> ready for sale.

Distillation Increases the Alcohol Concentration

1) Sometimes the products of fermentation are <u>distilled</u> to <u>increase</u> the <u>alcohol content</u>. This produces <u>spirits</u>, e.g. if <u>cane sugar</u> is fermented and then distilled, you get <u>rum</u>. <u>Fermented malted barley</u> is distilled to make <u>whisky</u>, and <u>fermented potatoes</u> are distilled to make <u>vodka</u>.

2) Distillation is used to <u>separate</u> the alcohol out of the alcohol-water solution that's produced by fermentation.

3) The fermentation products are <u>heated to 78 °C</u>, the temperature at which the alcohol (but not the water) boils and turns into vapour.

4) The <u>alcohol vapour rises</u> and travels through a cooled tube which causes it to <u>condense</u> back into <u>liquid alcohol</u> and run down the tube into a <u>collecting vessel</u>.

5) Alcohol can only be <u>distilled</u> on <u>licensed premises</u> — you're not allowed to do it in your garden shed.

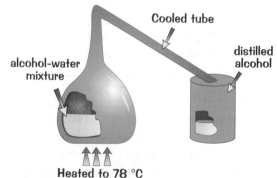

Cooled tube

distilled alcohol

alcohol-water mixture

Heated to 78 °C

"I should never have switched from Ribena to Vimto..."*

You can ferment pretty much <u>any kind of fruit</u> to make alcohol, e.g. cider is made from fermented apples. The <u>sugar</u> that yeast feeds on is naturally found in the fruit — you just have to <u>mash them</u> to get it out.

Using Micro-organisms — Biofuels

Biofuels are made from <u>living organisms' waste</u> or <u>dead plants</u>. Micro-organisms are used to <u>decompose</u> the plants and waste to create products such as <u>biogas</u> which can be used as fuel.

Biogas is Made Mainly of Methane

1) Biogas is usually about 70% <u>methane</u> (CH_4) and 30% <u>carbon dioxide</u> (CO_2). It also contains traces of <u>hydrogen</u>, <u>nitrogen</u> and <u>hydrogen sulfide</u>.

 Ka-boom

2) Biogas containing more than <u>50%</u> methane <u>burns easily</u>, but if it contains around <u>10%</u> methane it can be <u>explosive</u>.

3) Biogas is made by <u>bacteria</u> in a digester (see below). These bacteria are also found naturally in <u>marshes</u>, <u>septic tanks</u> and <u>animal digestive systems</u>. The bacteria's <u>respiration</u> produces methane.

Biogas Can be Used as Fuel

1) Biogas can be <u>burned</u> to power a <u>turbine</u>, which can be used to <u>generate electricity</u>. This is especially useful for producing electricity in <u>remote areas</u> with no mains supply.

2) Biogas can be <u>burned</u> to <u>heat water</u> and produce <u>steam</u> to heat <u>central heating systems</u>.

3) It can also be used as a <u>fuel</u> for <u>cars</u> and <u>buses</u>.

Biogas is Made by Anaerobic Fermentation of Waste Material

1) Biogas is made from plant waste and animal poo in a simple fermenter called a <u>digester</u>. <u>Sludge waste</u>, e.g. from <u>sewage works</u> or <u>sugar factories</u>, is used to make biogas on a <u>large scale</u>.

2) Several <u>different types of bacteria</u> are used to produce biogas. Some <u>decompose</u> the organic matter and produce waste, then another type decompose that waste, and so on, till you get biogas. This process is a <u>type of fermentation</u> — it involves the <u>breakdown of substances without oxygen</u>.

3) Biogas digesters need to be kept at a <u>constant warm temperature</u> (30-40 °C). This is the <u>optimum temperature</u> for the bacteria's <u>respiration</u>. Any <u>cooler</u> and the bacteria don't produce biogas as fast. Any <u>hotter</u> and the bacteria will be <u>killed</u>. The conditions in the digester also need to be <u>anaerobic</u>.

4) There are <u>two types</u> of biogas digester:

Batch digesters

<u>Batch digesters</u> make biogas in <u>small batches</u>. They're <u>manually loaded up with waste</u>, which is left to digest, and the digested material is cleared away at the end of each session.

Continuous digesters

<u>Continuous digesters</u> make biogas <u>all the time</u>. Waste is <u>continuously fed in</u>, and the biogas and digested material is <u>continuously removed</u> at a <u>steady rate</u>. Continuous digesters are more suited to <u>large-scale</u> biogas projects.

The diagram on the right shows a <u>simple biogas generator</u>. Whether it's a continuous or batch generator, it needs to have the following:

1) An inlet for <u>waste material</u> to be put in.

2) An outlet for the <u>digested material</u> to be removed through.

3) An outlet so that the <u>biogas</u> can be piped to where it's needed.

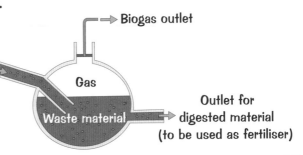

You can make biogas too — just eat some lentils...

Biogas isn't always a good thing — if it's released somewhere it shouldn't be it <u>can cause problems</u>. Methane is sometimes released from landfill sites and it can set alight and burn, or even <u>explode</u>. This can make a site unusable for many years, so a new site for dumping rubbish has to be found.

Using Micro-organisms — Biofuels

Biogas is better for the environment than burning fossil fuels. It's <u>sustainable</u> (unlike fossil fuels) and it's a <u>relatively clean fuel</u> — releasing fewer pollutants when burnt than oil and coal.

Biogas is a Sustainable Source of Energy

1) One big advantage of biogas over fossil fuels is that it's a <u>sustainable fuel</u>. The <u>plants</u> which are <u>decomposed</u> to <u>make biogas</u> can be <u>replaced quickly</u> with new crops. In contrast, there is a <u>finite</u> supply of <u>fossil fuels</u> like coal and crude oil — they will <u>run out</u> eventually.

2) Another advantage is that the <u>plants grown</u> to make biogas <u>photosynthesise</u> (see p.25), <u>removing CO_2</u> from the atmosphere. This <u>balances out</u> the <u>release of CO_2</u> from <u>burning the biogas</u>. Overall, using biogas doesn't release as much CO_2 into the atmosphere as burning <u>fossil fuels</u>. This is good because CO_2 is a '<u>greenhouse gas</u>' which contributes to <u>global warming</u>.

3) Biogas is a fairly <u>clean fuel</u>. Burning fossil fuels <u>produces particulates</u>, which can cause lung disease. Burning biogas <u>doesn't produce particulates</u>.

4) The use of biofuels <u>doesn't</u> produce significant amounts of sulfur dioxide or nitrogen oxides, which can cause <u>acid rain</u>. These are produced by power plants which burn fossil fuels.

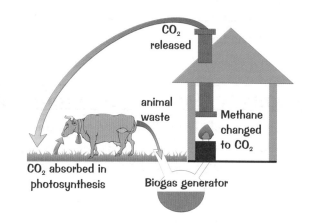

CO₂ released

animal waste

Methane changed to CO₂

CO₂ absorbed in photosynthesis

Biogas generator

5) The raw materials for biogas (plant waste or manure) are <u>cheap</u> and <u>readily available</u> (unlike fossil fuels like coal and crude oil which are relatively expensive and difficult to access).

6) Biogas generators act as a <u>waste disposal system</u>, getting rid of human and animal waste. Biogas is sometimes used as an energy source in <u>remote areas</u>, where there isn't a mains sewage system.

7) However, biogas <u>doesn't contain</u> as much <u>energy</u> as the same volume of <u>natural gas</u> (from underground supplies) because it's more dilute.

Ethanol Can be Used as a Biofuel

1) <u>Ethanol</u> can be burnt as <u>fuel</u>. It's a <u>cleaner fuel</u> than petrol or diesel, producing <u>fewer pollutants</u>.

2) <u>Ethanol</u> is a <u>renewable resource</u>. It is produced by using yeast to <u>ferment glucose</u> (see p.93). Materials like <u>sugar cane</u>, <u>corn</u> and <u>barley</u> can be used as a source of glucose in ethanol production.

3) <u>Cars</u> can be adapted to run on a <u>mixture of ethanol and petrol</u> — known as '<u>gasohol</u>'. Gasohol is a mixture of about 10% ethanol and 90% petrol.

4) Using gasohol <u>instead of pure petrol</u> means that <u>less crude oil</u> is being used up (petrol is refined from crude oil, which is a non-renewable energy source).

5) Another advantage is that the <u>growth of crops</u> for ethanol production means that <u>CO_2</u> is being <u>absorbed</u> from the atmosphere in photosynthesis. This goes some way towards balancing out the release of CO_2 when the gasohol is burnt.

6) Some countries, such as <u>Brazil</u>, have made extensive use of gasohol. It is most suitable for areas where there is <u>plenty of land</u> for growing crops for ethanol production.

There's an awful lot of biogas in Brazil...

Biogas probably isn't, sadly, the solution to <u>all</u> the world's energy needs. Some countries consume more energy than they could possibly get from biogas (because they <u>don't have the land</u> to grow enough crops). It's still a great way to get energy and dispose of waste in some areas though.

Life in Soil

Soil is made up of bits of <u>rock</u>, <u>dead material</u> (like dead leaves and animals), <u>living things</u>, <u>air</u> and <u>water</u>. Soil is teeming with life — insects, bacteria, worms and loads more icky creepy crawlies... eugh.

Soil is Full of Living Things

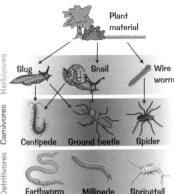

A soil food web

1) Soil may not look all that exciting, but it's pretty important to us. Plants need it for <u>anchorage</u> (to stop them falling over) and for a <u>supply of minerals</u> and <u>water</u>. And animals need plants for food and oxygen.

2) Soil is an ecosystem in itself, containing complex <u>food webs</u>. <u>Herbivores</u> (plant-eaters), <u>carnivores</u> (meat-eaters) and <u>detritivores</u> (which feed on dead organisms) are all found in the soil.

3) There are several other types of organism that live in the soil — <u>microscopic protozoans</u>, <u>fungi</u>, <u>nematode worms</u> and <u>bacteria</u>.

4) In order for a soil to support life, it must contain <u>water</u> and <u>oxygen</u>. All living things need water to <u>carry out reactions</u> in their cells, and cannot survive without it. Almost everything needs <u>oxygen</u> too, for <u>respiration</u> (see p.2). For example, the roots of plants need to get oxygen from the soil so they can respire.

Earthworms Help Keep Soil Healthy and Fertile

<u>Charles Darwin</u>, more famous for his theory of natural selection, spent an awful lot of his time <u>studying worms</u>. He observed them closely and experimented on them to see what sort of food they ate and how they behaved. He discovered these <u>reasons</u> why worms are <u>good for soil</u>:

1) Earthworms <u>bury leaves</u> and other <u>organic material</u> in the soil, where <u>bacteria</u> can <u>decompose them</u>.

2) Their <u>burrows</u> allow <u>air to enter the soil</u> and <u>water to drain through it</u>. Aeration provides the soil organisms with <u>oxygen</u>, but drainage is important, too — if the soil is <u>waterlogged</u>, there is <u>less oxygen</u> available.

3) They <u>mix up</u> the <u>soil layers</u>, <u>distributing</u> the <u>nutrients</u> more <u>equally</u>.

4) Soil in earthworm poo is <u>less acidic</u> than the soil they eat. This can help to <u>neutralise soil acidity</u>, although worms tend to avoid very acidic soils. Acidic soils are <u>less fertile</u> than neutral or alkaline soils.

<u>Farmers</u> and <u>gardeners</u> can <u>buy earthworms</u> (from worm farms) and add them to their soil to improve it.

Bacteria are Involved in Recycling Elements

1) Some elements are very important to living organisms, such as <u>nitrogen</u>, <u>sulfur</u> and <u>phosphorus</u>. Farmers sometimes add <u>fertiliser</u> (containing these elements) to the soil of their fields. But in the natural environment, there is no outside supply of these nutrients, so it's <u>essential</u> that they're <u>recycled</u>. If they weren't, they would <u>run out</u> and the plants would die... not good.

2) <u>Bacteria</u> are important in the recycling of elements, as many of them can change chemicals into other more useable ones. Different bacteria are involved in recycling different elements. E.g. in the <u>nitrogen cycle</u>, the following bacteria play a key part:

- <u>Saprophytic bacteria</u> in the soil start to <u>decompose dead material</u> into <u>ammonium compounds</u>.

- <u>Nitrifying bacteria</u>, such as <u>Nitrosomonas</u> and <u>Nitrobacter</u>. Nitrosomonas converts ammonium compounds into <u>nitrite</u>, and nitrobacter converts nitrite into <u>nitrate</u> (which plants can use).

- <u>Nitrogen-fixing bacteria</u> like <u>Azotobacter</u>, <u>Clostridium</u> and <u>Rhizobium</u>, convert <u>atmospheric nitrogen</u> into useful <u>nitrogen compounds</u>.

See p.73 for more on the nitrogen cycle.

Burying leaves — what a fun hobby...

In the exam you might get a question on <u>soil food webs</u>, e.g. 'What happens if you remove centipedes from the soil?' Well, the number of slugs and snails will increase (because fewer are being eaten) and the number of detritivores will go down (because they've got fewer dead centipedes to feed on).

Life in Water

Life in water is very different from life on land. The biggest challenge is regulating water content.

Living in Water Has Its Advantages...

1) One advantage of living in water is that there's a plentiful supply of water... unsurprisingly. There shouldn't be any danger of water shortage or dehydration (unless a drought makes streams dry up).

2) In water, there's less variation in temperature. Water doesn't heat up or cool down as quickly as air, so you don't normally get sudden temperature changes — which water life can find difficult to withstand.

3) Water provides support for plants and for animals that have no skeletal system. E.g. jellyfish are umbrella shaped in water (so they can swim) but if they get washed up on a beach they end up as quivering blobs, because there's not enough support... and then you stand on them. Ouch.

4) Waste disposal is easier. Poo and wee are easily dispersed. The loss of water in wee doesn't matter because there's plenty of water about to make up for it.

...and Its Disadvantages

1) Water is more resistant to movement than air, so animals living in water have to use more energy to move about. Think how much effort it takes to walk in the sea compared to walking on the beach.

2) Aquatic animals have to be able to control the amount of water in their body (water regulation). This is because the water an animal lives in has a different concentration of solutes from the animal's cells. If the animal couldn't regulate water, water molecules would enter or leave the animal's cells by osmosis to even up the solute concentrations. This would cause damage to the cells. E.g.

- If the animal lived in salt-water its cells would probably contain a lower solute concentration than the surrounding water. If the animal wasn't able to regulate water, then water molecules would leave its cells by osmosis, causing them to shrivel and die.

- If the animal lived in freshwater, its cells would probably contain a higher solute concentration than the surrounding water. If the animal wasn't able to regulate water, then water molecules would enter its cells by osmosis, causing them to swell and burst.

Water Content is Regulated in Different Ways

1) The kidneys of fish are specially adapted to either salt-water or freshwater to ensure that the concentration of water in the blood remains constant. Some types of fish move between salt-water and freshwater environments and need further adaptations, e.g.

> Salmon live in the sea but move into freshwater rivers to breed.
> Their hormones adjust their bodies to cope with the different environments.

2) Single-celled organisms, like amoebas, only have a cell membrane between them and the surrounding water. They use a different method of water regulation:

> Amoebas regulate water with a contractile vacuole which collects the water that diffuses in by osmosis. The vacuole then moves to the cell membrane and contracts to empty the water outside the cell.

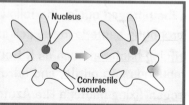

Nucleus

Contractile vacuole

"Waiter, do you have frog's legs?" — "No, I always walk like this"...

Some organisms (mainly insects and amphibians) spend part of their life cycle in water and part on land to exploit both habitats. The two environments provide different challenges, so the different parts of the life cycle often have different body forms (e.g. tadpole and frog).

Module B6 — Beyond the Microscope

Life in Water

There are monsters in the water. Millions of them. They're only tiny, mind...

Plankton are Microscopic Organisms That Live in Water

1) Plankton are <u>microscopic</u> organisms that live in <u>fresh</u> and <u>salt water</u>. There are <u>two</u> types:
   - <u>Phytoplankton</u> are microscopic <u>plants</u>.
   - <u>Zooplankton</u> are microscopic <u>animals</u>. Zooplankton <u>feed on</u> phytoplankton.

2) Phytoplankton <u>photosynthesise</u> and are the main <u>producers</u> in <u>aquatic food webs</u>, so they're very important in both freshwater and salt-water ecosystems.

3) Plankton <u>can't move far</u> by themselves and so rely on <u>water currents</u> to carry them from place to place.

4) <u>Phytoplankton</u> populations usually <u>increase</u> between late <u>spring</u> and late <u>summer</u>. This is called an <u>algal bloom</u> (phytoplankton are a type of algae). An algal bloom makes the water go all green and murky.

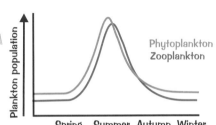

   The increase is due to <u>longer, sunnier days</u> in summer:
   - <u>More light</u> is available for <u>photosynthesis</u> and the energy is used for <u>growth</u>.
   - <u>Temperatures increase</u>, causing both <u>photosynthesis</u> and <u>growth rates</u> to increase.

   The population of <u>zooplankton</u> also <u>increases</u> because there is <u>more phytoplankton</u> to <u>feed on</u>.

5) An increase in <u>nitrates</u> and <u>phosphates</u> also causes algal blooms because the phytoplankton have <u>more nutrients</u>. It happens when water is <u>polluted</u> by <u>fertilisers</u> or <u>sewage</u>.

> You might be asked to <u>interpret marine food webs</u> in the exam. Think about how other organisms in the food chain will be affected by an <u>increase/decrease of plankton</u>. If their food source decreases, so will their population. Keep your eye on what <u>season</u> it is too.

There are Several Causes of Water Pollution

1) Fertilisers and Sewage

Pollution of water by fertilisers and sewage causes <u>eutrophication</u>.

| Fertilisers and sewage enter water, adding extra nutrients | → | Algal bloom | → | Algae die | → | Bacteria feed on dead algae, using up all the oxygen in the water | → | Organisms that need oxygen, e.g. fish, die. |

Some organisms are particularly sensitive to the <u>level of oxygen</u> in the water. These species are used by scientists to <u>indicate how polluted the water is</u> (the less oxygen, the more polluted). For this reason they're called <u>indicator species</u>.

Pollution level	Indicator species
Clean	Stonefly nymph, Mayfly nymph
Low	Freshwater shrimp, Caddis fly larva
High	Bloodworm, Waterlouse
Very high	Rat-tailed maggot, sludgeworm

2) Industrial Chemicals and Pesticides

Chemicals which have caused water pollution include <u>pesticides</u> like <u>DDT</u> (used to kill lice and mosquitoes) and <u>industrial chemicals</u> like <u>PCBs</u> (used as coolants and electrical insulators). If <u>water</u> is <u>polluted</u> by these, they are <u>taken up</u> by <u>organisms</u> at the bottom of the food chain. They <u>aren't broken down</u> by the organisms, so when they're eaten the chemical is <u>passed on</u>. The <u>concentration</u> of the chemical <u>increases</u> as it is transferred <u>up the food chain</u> — because each organism eats many of the organisms below it. Organisms at the <u>top of the food chain</u>, e.g. whales, <u>accumulate</u> a <u>huge dose</u> and may die.

3) Oil

Spills from <u>oil tanker accidents</u> and also oil from <u>boat engines</u> harm water life.

<u>Acid rain</u> is another source of water pollution.

Mouldy pizza — indicator species for dirty bedrooms...

In the exam, you might be given some pollution data and asked to identify the <u>source</u> of the pollution. Look out for factories, farms, sewage plants/pipes and oil tankers lurking around suspiciously.

Enzymes in Action

Enzymes are molecules made of <u>protein</u>, which <u>speed up (catalyse) chemical reactions</u> in living organisms. Scientists know a good thing when they see it, and enzymes are now used for all sorts of stuff...

Enzymes are Used in <u>Biological Washing Powder...</u>

1) Some stains are caused by <u>soluble</u> chemicals and so they <u>wash out</u> easily in water. Stubborn stains contain <u>insoluble chemicals</u> like starch, proteins and fats. They don't wash out with just water.

2) <u>Non-biological washing powders</u> (detergents) contain <u>chemicals</u> that break up <u>stains</u> on your clothes.

3) <u>Biological washing powders</u> contain the same chemicals as non-biological ones, but also contain a mixture of <u>enzymes</u> which break down the stubborn stains.

Stain	Sources of stain	Enzymes	Product
Carbohydrate	Jam, chocolate	Amylases	Simple sugars
Lipid (fats)	Butter, oil	Lipases	Fatty acids and glycerol
Protein	Blood, grass	Proteases	Amino acids

 The <u>products</u> of the enzyme-controlled reactions are <u>soluble in water</u> and so can be easily washed out of the material.

4) Biological washing powders need a <u>cooler wash temperature</u> than non-biological powders because the enzymes are <u>denatured</u> (destroyed) by <u>high temperatures</u> (see p.38). However, some newer powders contain enzymes that are <u>more resistant</u> to heat and so can be used with a hotter water temperature.

5) The enzymes <u>work best</u> at <u>pH 7</u> (neutral). Tap water is usually about pH 7, but in areas with very hard water (water containing high levels of calcium) it might be alkaline, which can damage the enzymes.

6) You can buy <u>special stain removers</u> (e.g. for wine, blood or oil). Some of these are just special solvents, but some contain <u>specific enzymes</u> that will break down the stain.

...and in <u>Medical Products...</u>

1) <u>Diabetes</u> (see p.14) is <u>diagnosed</u> by the presence of <u>sugar</u> in the <u>urine</u>. Many years ago, doctors actually used to taste patients' urine to test for sugar... yuk. Later they tested the urine for sugar using <u>Benedict's solution</u>. When it's heated, the solution <u>changes colour</u> from blue to orange if sugar is <u>present</u>. This test relies on chemical properties (not enzymes).

2) Nowadays, <u>reagent strips</u> (strips of paper with enzymes and chemicals in them) are used. They're dipped in urine and <u>change colour</u> if sugar is <u>present</u>.

3) This test is based on a sequence of <u>enzyme reactions</u>. The product of the enzyme-controlled reactions causes a chemical embedded in the strip to change colour.

4) There are similar strips which can be used to test <u>blood sugar levels</u> (see next page).

...and in the <u>Food Industry</u>

Low-Calorie Food	1) <u>Table sugar</u> (<u>sucrose</u>) is what you normally <u>sweeten food with</u> at home. 2) In the food industry an enzyme called <u>invertase</u> is used to <u>break down sucrose</u> into <u>glucose</u> and <u>fructose</u>. Glucose and fructose are <u>much sweeter</u> than sucrose. 3) This means you can get the same level of sweetness using <u>less sugar</u>. This helps to make <u>low-calorie food sweeter</u> without adding calories.
Cheese	The enzyme <u>rennet</u> is used to <u>clot milk</u> in the first stages of <u>cheese production</u>.
Juice Extraction	The enzyme <u>pectinase</u> is used in <u>fruit juice extraction</u>. It breaks down <u>pectin</u> (a part of the cell wall in apples and oranges), causing the cell to release its juice.

Stubborn stains — not just dirty, but grumpy...

Not everyone can use biological washing powders. Some of the enzymes remain on the clothes and can irritate sensitive skin, making it sore and itchy. Sensitive people have to use non-biological powders.

Enzymes in Action

When enzymes are used to speed up reactions, they end up <u>dissolved in the mixture</u> with the substrates and products — and can be <u>difficult to remove</u>. One way to avoid this is to <u>immobilise</u> the enzymes...

Immobilising Enzymes Makes Them Easier to Remove

1) Many industrial processes use <u>immobilised enzymes</u>, which <u>don't</u> need to be <u>separated out</u> from the mixture after the reaction has taken place.

2) Immobilised enzymes are <u>attached</u> to an <u>insoluble material</u>, e.g. <u>fibres</u> (like collagen or cellulose), or <u>silica gel</u>. Or they are encapsulated in <u>alginate beads</u> (alginate is a gel-like substance).

3) The immobilised enzymes are <u>still active</u> and still help speed up reactions.

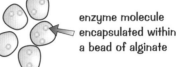
enzyme molecule encapsulated within a bead of alginate

Advantages of Immobilising Enzymes

1) The insoluble material with attached enzymes can be washed and <u>reused</u>.

2) The enzymes <u>don't contaminate</u> the product.

3) Immobilised enzymes are often more <u>stable</u> and less likely to denature at high temperatures or extremes of pH.

Immobilised Enzymes Can be Used to Make Lactose-Free Milk

1) The sugar <u>lactose</u> is naturally found in <u>milk</u> (and yoghurt). It's broken down in your digestive system by the <u>enzyme lactase</u>. This produces <u>glucose</u> and <u>galactose</u>, which are then <u>absorbed</u> into the blood.

2) Some people <u>lack the enzyme lactase</u>. If they drink milk the lactose isn't broken down and gut <u>bacteria</u> feed on it, causing <u>abdominal pain</u>, <u>wind</u> and <u>diarrhoea</u> — these people are <u>lactose intolerant</u>.

3) <u>Cats</u> are also lactose intolerant (which is odd considering how much they like milk). They can't digest lactose and have the same symptoms as humans if they drink it.

4) <u>Lactose-free milk</u> can be produced using <u>immobilised lactase</u>. (Special <u>lactose-free cats' milk</u> is also produced using lactase.)

5) A method called <u>continuous flow processing</u> is often used for this:

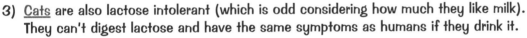
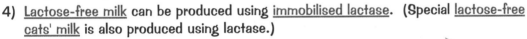
Column of immobilised lactase

Lactose free milk

- The substrate solution (milk) is run through a <u>column of immobilised enzymes</u>.
- The enzymes convert the substrate (lactose) into the products (glucose and galactose), but only the <u>products</u> emerge from the column. The enzymes stay fixed in the column.

Immobilised Enzymes are Also Used in Reagent Strips

1) <u>Diabetics</u> use reagent strips to measure their <u>blood glucose concentration</u> on a <u>daily basis</u>. They're <u>quick</u> and <u>convenient</u> to use. Before reagent strips diabetics had to 'guess' when they needed to inject insulin (e.g. before meals), because there was no quick way of knowing what their glucose level was.

2) There are <u>immobilised enzymes</u> on the reagent strips.

3) A drop of blood from a finger prick is added to the strip. The enzymes in the strip cause it to <u>change different colours</u> depending on the <u>glucose concentration</u>. The colour is then compared to a <u>chart</u> to find out the level of blood sugar.

You treat your cat with milk — he thanks you with diarrhoea...

Lactose intolerance affects <u>millions of people</u>. There's a pretty big industry out there providing them with lactose-free milk, lactose-free ice cream, lactose-free chocolates...

More on Genetic Engineering

You've already learnt about genetic engineering in Module B3, but there's more detail in this Module.

Genes Can be Transferred Between Different Organisms

1) Genes from one organism will often work in another one.
2) Genetic engineering alters the genetic code of an organism. A gene giving a desirable characteristic is removed from one organism and inserted into another organism.
3) The genetically modified organism is called a transgenic organism.
4) The two main uses of genetic engineering are to produce medicines and to produce better crops.

Bacteria Can be Engineered to Produce Human Insulin

The idea is to put the human insulin gene into bacteria so that the bacteria can make human insulin. The modified bacteria reproduce, and you end up with millions of insulin-producing bacteria.

1) Scientists identify the gene which controls the production of human insulin. They remove it from the DNA of the human cell by 'cutting' it out with restriction enzymes.

2) A loop of bacterial DNA (called a plasmid) is then prepared for the insulin gene to be inserted. Enzymes are used to cut open the plasmid.

3) The insulin gene is inserted in the plasmid. Another enzyme called ligase is used to join the inserted gene to the bacterial DNA.

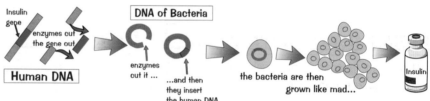

4) The bacteria are checked using assaying techniques to make sure they contain the new gene.

5) The bacteria are then cultivated to produce millions of identical bacteria, all making human insulin.

6) This can be done on an industrial scale and the insulin can be separated out.

Crops Can be Genetically Modified (GM)

1) Some plants are naturally more resistant to disease and weedkillers than others. The genes that cause resistance can be removed and inserted into commercial plants — creating new disease-resistant and weedkiller-resistant versions.

2) Plants can be engineered to grow in poor conditions, e.g. in salty-water or drought conditions.

3) Production of crops can be increased by genetically engineering them to grow faster and bigger.

4) Plants can be genetically modified to be more nutritious as food, e.g. GM rice which contains a chemical that humans can turn into vitamin A.

5) Genetically engineered strains of plants such as soya beans, maize and cotton are already grown in many countries, e.g. Canada, USA, Argentina, Spain, India, Indonesia, China and Australia.

There are Advantages and Disadvantages

1) There are plenty of advantages to this technology — crop yield is increased (which means cheaper food for us), places with poor farming conditions can grow crops and crops can be made more nutritious.

2) There are risks though — there may be unexpected harmful effects of changing an organism's genes. There's more about this on p.54.

I wish they could insert a revising gene into my brain...

Clotting factors to treat haemophilia (a blood clotting disorder) are made in exactly the same way as human insulin. The gene is inserted into bacteria, which then produce it. It's so darn clever.

Revision Summary for Module B6

I bet you thought you'd never get to the end of this book... well, here you are and there's just one more revision summary to go. I never knew how interesting micro-organisms could be, they do so many things — making yoghurt, causing disease, clearing up sugar spills, making booze, biogas and insulin. And as for those useful enzymes... they're a barrel of laughs.

1) State the function of the following parts of a bacterial cell: a) flagellum, b) cell wall, c) bacterial DNA.
2) Describe the main stages in making yoghurt.
3) Describe the four stages in an infectious disease.
4) Suggest two reasons why the incidence of cholera and dysentery might be high in a given population.
5) Explain why natural disasters often cause rapid spread of disease.
6) How are antiseptics and antibiotics used to control disease?
7) Describe how Alexander Fleming discovered penicillin.
8) State the word equations for anaerobic respiration and aerobic respiration in yeast.
9) How is the rate of breakdown of sugar by yeast affected by temperature? Sketch a graph to illustrate your answer.
10) Describe the main stages in brewing beer.
11) How could you increase the alcohol concentration of a fermented product?
12) Name three natural sources of biogas.
13) List three uses of biogas.
14) Explain how and why biogas production is affected by temperature.
15) List five advantages of biogas.
16) Explain what gasohol is and how it's made.
17) Draw a typical soil food web. Label the herbivores, carnivores and detritivores.
18) Describe four ways in which earthworms improve soil fertility.
19) Describe how bacteria in the soil are involved in recycling nitrogen.
    Name one example of each type of bacterium.
20) Name two advantages and two disadvantages of living in water.
21) How do amoebas regulate their water content?
22) What water-related problem faces salmon? How do they overcome it?
23) Explain what an algal boom is.
24) Why do algal blooms normally occur in late spring to late summer?
25) Explain the process of eutrophication. Name two things that can cause it.
26) Explain how industrial chemicals and pesticides can kill species at the top of the food chain.
27) Which enzyme in biological powder would break down a stain made of: a) butter, b) grass?
28) Why do biological washing powders need a cool wash temperature and neutral pH?
29) Name an enzyme that breaks down sucrose. What is this enzyme used for in the food industry?
30) Give three advantages of immobilising enzymes.
31) What is lactose intolerance?
32) How is lactose-free cat's milk made?
33) How are bacteria genetically engineered to produce human insulin?
34) Describe three ways in which crops can be improved by genetic engineering.

Thinking in Exams

In the old days, it was enough to learn a whole bunch of <u>facts</u> while you were revising and just spew them onto the paper come exam day. If you knew the facts, you had a good chance of doing well, even if you didn't really <u>understand</u> what any of those facts actually meant. But those days are over. Rats.

Remember — You Might Have to Think During the Exam

1) Nowadays, the examiners want you to be able to <u>apply</u> your scientific knowledge to newspaper articles you're reading or to situations you've <u>not met</u> before. Eeek.

2) The trick is <u>not</u> to <u>panic</u>. They're <u>not</u> expecting you to show Einstein-like levels of scientific insight (not usually, anyway).

3) They're just expecting you to use the science you <u>know</u> in an <u>unfamiliar setting</u> — and usually they'll give you some <u>extra info</u> too that you should use in your answer.

So to give you an idea of what to expect come exam-time, use the new <u>CGP Exam Simulator</u> (below). Read the article, and have a go at the questions. It's <u>guaranteed</u> to be just as much fun as the real thing.

Underlining or making notes of the main bits as you read is a good idea.

1. Blood glucose levels controlled by insulin.

2. Insulin added
→ liver removes glucose.

3. Not enough insulin
→ high blood glucose
→ death?

4. Carbohydrates cause problems for diabetics. So carbohydrates and glucose linked...

All cells need energy to function, and this energy is supplied by glucose carried in the blood. The level of glucose in the blood is controlled by the hormone insulin — if the <u>blood glucose level gets too high, insulin is introduced</u> into the bloodstream, which in turn <u>makes the liver remove glucose.</u>

Diabetes (type I) is where <u>not enough insulin is produced</u>, meaning that a person's <u>blood glucose level can rise</u> to a level that can <u>kill</u> them. The problem can be controlled in two ways:

a) Avoiding foods rich in carbohydrates. It can also be helpful to take exercise after eating <u>carbohydrates</u>.

b) Injecting insulin before meals (especially if high in <u>carbohydrates</u>).

<u>Questions</u>:

1. Why can it be helpful for a diabetic to take exercise after eating carbohydrates?

2. Suggest why a diabetic person should make sure they eat sensibly after injecting insulin.

3. Dave Edwards, a leading diabetes specialist, has made a new discovery about the condition. He decides to share his findings with the scientific community. Suggest two ways he could do this.

Clues — don't read unless you need a bit of a hand...

1. More complex carbohydrates are broken down to make glucose. What would normally happen if lots of glucose is suddenly put into the blood? How would this normally be controlled? And what happens in a diabetic?

2. Think about what insulin causes to happen.

3. This isn't a trick question — think of how you'd expect to read or hear about scientific discoveries.

Answers

1) Eating carbohydrates puts a lot of glucose into the blood. Exercising can use up extra glucose, which helps stop blood glucose levels getting too high.

2) If they don't, blood glucose levels can drop dangerously low.

3) Any two sensible means of communication, e.g. conference, internet, book, journal, phone, meeting.

Thinking in an exam — it's not like the old days...

It's scary — being expected to <u>think</u> in the exam. But questions like this often have half the answers in the passage they give you — so just <u>take your time</u>, <u>think things through</u> and you'll be fine.

Answering Experiment Questions

Science is all (well... a lot) about <u>doing experiments carefully</u>, and <u>interpreting results</u>.
And so that's what they're going to test you on when you do your exam. Among other things.

Read the Question *Carefully*

Expect at least some questions to describe experiments — a bit like the one below.

> Pu-lin did an experiment to see how the mass of a potato changed depending on the sugar solution it was in.
>
> She started off by making potato tubes 5 cm in length, 1 cm in diameter and 2.0 g in mass. She then filled a beaker with 500 cm^3 of pure water and placed a potato tube in it for 30 minutes. She repeated the experiment with different amounts of sugar dissolved in the water. For each potato tube, she measured the new mass.
>
> These are the results Pu-lin obtained:

Number of teaspoons of sugar	0	2	4	6	8	10	12	14	16	18	20
Mass of potato tube (g)	2.50	2.40	2.23	2.10	2.02	1.76	1.66	1.55	1.47	1.3	1.15

a) State one way that Pu-lin helped to make it a fair test.

   She used the same volume of water each time.

> To make it a <u>fair test</u>, you've got to keep <u>all</u> the other variables the same so you're <u>only changing one thing</u>. That way you know that there's <u>only thing</u> that can be affecting the result.
>
> Other answers could be: size of potato tubes, shape of potato tubes or length of time.

b) A graph of these results is plotted below.

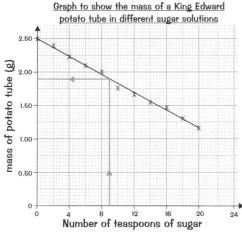

Graph to show the mass of a King Edward potato tube in different sugar solutions

> This is a <u>scattergram</u> — they're used to see if two variables are <u>related</u>.

> 1) <u>Draw a line</u> on the graph <u>up</u> from the value you know.
> 2) Where it <u>hits the line</u>, follow it <u>across</u> to the <u>other axis</u> and <u>read off</u> the corresponding value.

c) Estimate the mass of the potato tube if you added nine teaspoons of sugar.

   Estimate of mass = *1.90 g (see graph)*

d) What can you conclude from these results?

   There is a relationship between the number of teaspoons of sugar and the mass of potato tube. Each additional teaspoon causes the potato tube to lose more mass.

> In lab-based experiments like this one, you can say that one variable <u>causes</u> the other one to change. The extra sugar <u>causes</u> the potato to lose mass. You can say this because everything else has <u>stayed the same</u> — nothing else could be causing the change.

Don't go testing things on your brother — that's not fair...

You've got to get used to dealing with <u>graphs</u>. Biology's <u>full of experiments</u> where relationships aren't obvious — so you have to <u>make measurements</u> and <u>interpret</u> the <u>results</u>. Guaranteed to be in the exam.

Index

Index

Index and Answers

Answers

Revision Summary for Module B1 (page 20)

2) a) Students. Group B have higher blood pressures so they are likely to be the teachers because your blood pressure increases with age.
   b) 2.
   c) E.g. cut alcohol and salt intake, do more exercise, reduce stress levels, lose any excess weight.

33)

Revision Summary for Module B2 (page 34)

11) E.g. 1. Does it have a shell?　Yes — it's a snail
　　　　　　　　　　　　　　　No — go to question 2.
　　2. Does it have legs?　No — it's a worm
　　　　　　　　　　　　　Yes — go to question 3.
　　3. Does it have more than 8 legs?　Yes — it's a centipede
　　　　　　　　　　　　　　　　No — it's a spider.

13) Population size = $\frac{23 \times 28}{4}$ = 161